THE
NEW
BEAUTY
BOOK

THE NEW BEAUTY BOOK

ALEXANDRA CRUICKSHANK

ARTUS

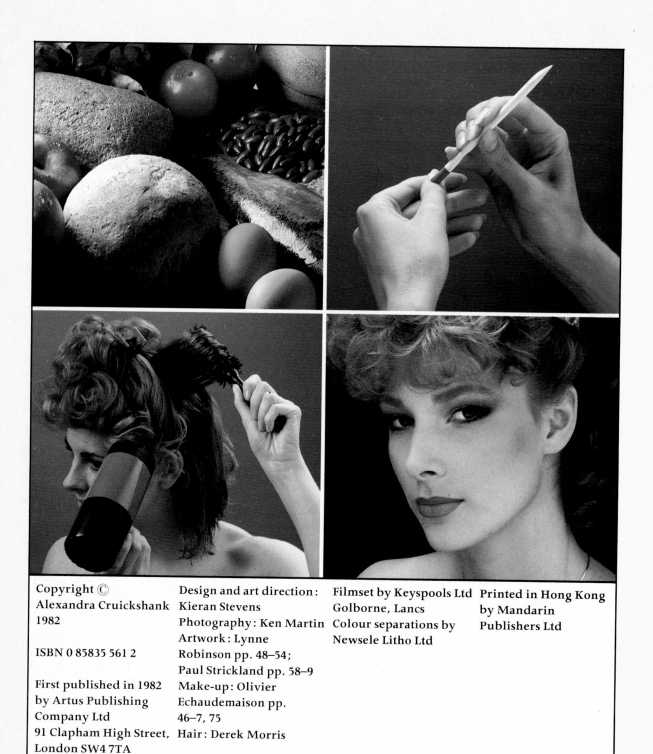

Design and art direction: Kieran Stevens
Photography: Ken Martin
Artwork: Lynne Robinson pp. 48–54; Paul Strickland pp. 58–9
Make-up: Olivier Echaudemaison pp. 46–7, 75
Hair: Derek Morris

Filmset by Keyspools Ltd Golborne, Lancs
Colour separations by Newsele Litho Ltd

Printed in Hong Kong by Mandarin Publishers Ltd

CONTENTS

The author wishes to thank the following for their expert help in
the preparation of this book:
Rita Roberts, Director of the Clinical Cosmetic Centre in London
Jacqueline Burgess Wall, Director of the London Beauty Studio
Daniel Galvin, hairdresser and colouring expert of Daniel Galvin, London
Olivier Echaudemaison, Creative Director of the Harriet Hubbard Ayer
Cosmetic House, Paris
The British Nutrition Foundation, London
David Lieber, Director of the Morlé Slimming and Beauty Centre, London
Joan Price, Director of The Face Place, London

INTRODUCTION

Always fascinating, constantly expanding, the world of beauty has come to mean a lot more than simply choosing the newest make-up colours or learning how to cultivate long fingernails and lustrous hair. Beauty of course is still fun – but it's no longer superficial. Learning to look and feel one's best has become a serious, sometimes complex subject that affects almost all women whatever their age, type or lifestyle.

Beauty and health these days go hand in hand. The finest cosmetics in the world cannot disguise the effects of poor nutrition, lack of sleep and exercise or too much stress. After all, good health radiates its own special glow that you cannot buy in a pot. It is reflected in a clear skin, sparkling eyes, glossy hair and a fit, trim body. Beauty today is also a highly scientific subject; modern technology has helped doctors and beauticians to understand and treat more successfully a whole host of common problems from acne and dehydrated skin to headaches and other stress-related aches and pains. For example, by learning more about how too much sunlight, central heating and cigarette smoking can dry and age the skin,

it is becoming a lot easier to prevent many beauty problems from occurring in the first place.

Modern beauty products and techniques are a lot more effective and accessible than they were a few years ago, and because of this women's scope for self-improvement is far greater. Individualism has become the keynote to looking good, and rigid make-up and hairdressing rules along with ideal model girl looks and proportions are, thank goodness, a thing of the past. Improving on nature I believe means adapting modern trends to suit your own personality, taking your pick of the most effective methods available for enhancing good features as well as improving or minimizing those that are less than perfect.

As a health and beauty writer I'm continually reminded that the beauty world changes rapidly, and to keep up with the pace I've consulted leading specialists in each of the major areas from hair care to exercise. I extend a warm and grateful thanks to all of these experts for helping me, and therefore you, to keep a finger on the pulse of beauty in the 1980s, and for explaining what it really takes to look – and feel – our very best.

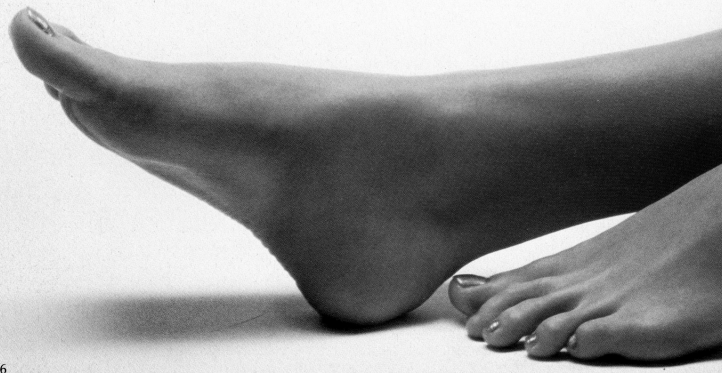

YOUR BODY-
YOUR BASIC MATERIAL

Beauty and health are almost totally inter-dependent. It's impossible to divide one from the other, since every inch of our outer 'envelope' – our skin, hair, eyes and figure – is a reflection of our physical health and emotional well-being. You certainly don't have to be a hypochondriac to be tuned into your body and take care of how it looks and feels. Being health-and-beauty conscious inevitably involves a degree of pride and self-esteem, as well as working out how we truly wish to appear to ourselves and the rest of the world – then making a concentrated effort to achieve that goal. Most doctors agree that a streak of vanity – provided it's held in check and doesn't lapse into obsession – is essentially a sign of a healthy, well-balanced ego. Indeed hospital staff generally recognize a woman's renewed interest in her face and hair as an important sign of recovery after a long illness.

The nitty-gritty of beauty therefore often begins with how well you feel. Generally speaking, the smoother the overall condition of the body, the less likely you are to suffer from many common figure and beauty complaints. We are not, after all, a collection of spare, uncoordinated parts; because each organ and system within the body interacts with all the others, any physical weakness or imbalance will eventually be reflected in the condition of the skin, hair, nails, eyes and figure. Because of their effect on hormone secretion, nerve impulses, digestion and elimination, your state of mind and the harmony between brain and central nervous system play a particularly important role in governing your looks. A severe emotional shock can have great physical repercussions; altering the hormone levels of the body and therefore disrupting the menstrual cycle and the complexion. Our bodies constantly reflect the ups and downs of diet, illness and stress.

SKIN - A LARGE COMPLEX ORGAN

No other part of our bodies records shifting patterns of health as accurately as the skin. A smooth, radiant, trouble-free complexion is, as it was centuries ago, one of a woman's most valued and desirable possessions. Yet few of us are born with impeccable skin, and a good complexion more often than not needs to be cultivated with care and patience. Just as revealing is the fact that those women who *are* blessed with a naturally beautiful skin must work to care for and protect it almost as much as anyone else in order to safeguard its quality and youthful appearance.

The skin is one of the most complex organs and hard-working systems of the human body. Spread flat it would cover roughly 1.6 sq m (17 sq ft), and, if you could find a microscope powerful enough, you would see that a 2 sq cm piece of skin (just under a square inch) is packed with about a dozen blood vessels, 25 nerve endings, 100 sweat glands, hair follicles, sebaceous glands, muscles, pores and more than three million cells, all constantly dying and renewing themselves. Skin is about 20 per cent fluid, and accounts for around 2.7 kg (6 lb) of body weight. It is continuously expanding and contracting, eliminating waste matter and keeping an automatic check on the temperature of the body. As well as providing us with very pretty outer wrapping, skin is also the hardiest, most effective form of protective packaging ever invented.

ON THE LEVEL

Surface skin is made up of the stratum corneum or epidermis – a fine layer of flattened, overlapping dead cells that's continually being shed as new cells die and are pushed upwards from beneath the skin's surface. Dead as it is, the basic condition of the epidermis is what determines the aesthetic quality of your skin.

It takes about three weeks for young healthy skin to fully renew itself, but this slows down as early as the late twenties or early thirties, heralding the first visible signs of skin ageing. Beneath the surface skin lies the dermis, a priceless reservoir of moisture, protein, living cells, oil glands and capillaries, that keep the skin moist, well-toned, unlined and glowing. The deepest layer, the hypodermis, contains chiefly fat cells and muscle, giving the skin of the face and body its contour and underlying support structure. In terms of preserving young, beautiful skin, scientists have now established that what really counts is how promptly and efficiently cells renew themselves, the balance of moisture in the epidermis, and the strength and suppleness of the collagen fibres and interweaving elastic fibres which determine the skin's elasticity and smoothness. So, although the quality of our skin depends largely on how we care for its surface over the years, its basic characteristics, overall state and rate of ageing are thought to be determined more by the health and condition of these deeper layers. What's more, it's an established medical fact that strong sunlight, smoking, drinking too much alcohol, crash dieting, exposure to central heating and air conditioning, and prolonged bouts of illness and stress can drastically rob your skin of its moisture reserves and thereby cause it to begin ageing prematurely, unless you take steps to protect it.

Rita Roberts, one of England's most respected beauty therapists and teachers, has spent over thirty years unravelling the clues to common skin problems. She stresses that the fate of our complexion lies more often than not squarely in our own hands – its condition dependent to a large extent on how accurately we identify our own skin type and accordingly how careful we are in meeting its requirements in terms of proper cleansing, diet, exercise and rest.

FINDING YOUR TYPE

Just like bone structure and colouring, your basic skin type is almost entirely hereditary. It determines not only the products and routine that keep your complexion looking its best, but also provides invaluable advance warning of the sort of skin problems you may meet at some time during your life. Finding your

At any age, a glowing, flawless complexion is a priceless asset. It needs cultivation as well as lifelong care.

Skin type	Cleansing	Toning	Moisturizing
oily and coloured	detergent-free soap and water and/or cleansing milk	cucumber or witch hazel skin tonic	fine, non-greasy, oil-oil-in-water emulsion
normal	detergent-free soap and/or cleansing milk, as preferred	mild, alcohol-free tonic	will suit any type of moisturizer
dry	cleansing milk, cream or lotion, applied with cotton wool or tissue	mild skin freshener to ensure that all traces of cleanser have been removed; mineral water spray	richer, 'water-in-oil' cream or lotion
combination	detergent-free soap and water	mild skin freshener on dry areas, with stronger tonic for greasy panel	oil-free moisturizer with perhaps a richer cream for dry areas
sensitive and allergy-prone	cleansing milk or lightweight lotion applied with cotton wool	alcohol-free skin freshener or mineral water spray	lightweight, fragrance-free, oil-in-water moisturizer, preferably hypo-allergenic

Complexion brushes and exfoliating creams can improve the complexion considerably by lifting off dead surface skin and stimulating the layer beneath.

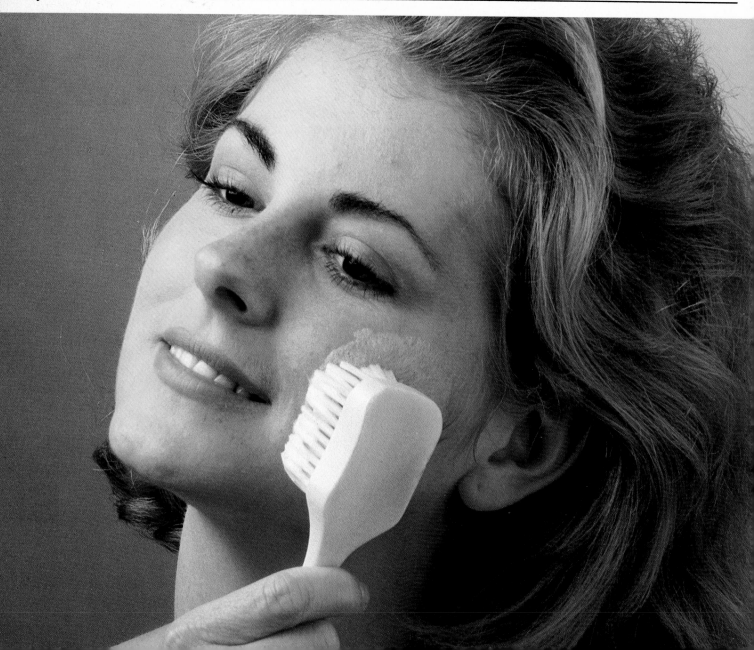

skin type is a relatively simple procedure. You've probably heard of the tissue test and the sellotape guide which aim to identify the oily and dry areas of your face and therefore your skin type. Both are apt to be confusing and often not as reliable as plain visual scrutiny. After you have thoroughly cleansed your face and applied moisturizer, wait thirty to forty-five minutes, then take a look in the mirror. If your face is beginning to shine all over and the pores are clearly visible, you probably have an oily skin – prone to spots, blackheads and other pore problems. If only the centre forehead, nose and chin are shiny, the rest of the face matt, then yours is a combination skin – normal or dry with an oily 'T' zone. Normal skin generally looks matt with a slight peach-bloom finish that reflects the light and has no visible pores – or obvious problems. Dry skin on the other hand is often taut, fine or transparent with slightly flaky patches on the cheeks and prone to tiny lines even after you've applied moisturizer. Very sensitive and allergy-prone skin is fine to the point of translucence with a tendency to dryness, a red tone and broken red veins. This type of skin needs to be protected like precious porcelain; it may react by breaking out in rashes, spots and redness with certain, rich perfumed cosmetics. Broken veins are the real long-term problem of this skin type, so very drying conditions, extremes of hot and cold and over-vigorous, abrasive treatment must be avoided at all costs. Luckily there is an increasing number of excellent, gentle, hypo-allergenic, fragrance-free cosmetics on the market today which are specially designed to care for very delicate skins.

The darker skin tones (everything from olive to brown and black) invariably tend to be on the oily side and not prone to flakiness or extreme sensitivity. This is because on the whole dark skin is coarser and thicker than very pale skin, while the added pigmentation acts as a natural protection against the 'weathering' effects of sunlight and harsh, dry climates.

CLEANSING
the top priority

The importance of thorough, twice-daily cleansing cannot be stressed enough – regardless of whether or not you wear make-up. Since the skin is an organ of elimination, anything obstructing this function, such as stale make-up, old face cream or just general grime, will not only result in blocked pores, which can cause spots and blackheads, but will also accumulate, leaving a drab, muddy-looking complexion. Furthermore, for any skincare product such as a moisturizer to penetrate the skin's surface and get to work properly, the surface must be totally cleansed of all obstructing creams and debris.

Many people still automatically equate cleansing with soap and water, though the debate on the pros and cons of the effects of washing the face continues unresolved. Certainly you should avoid using very harsh, scummy, perfumed soap on your face, since this will only irritate and dry out the skin. However, there's little to beat a good lather and splashes of water for making the skin feel truly clean and refreshed; something leading cosmetic manufacturers have all latched onto in recent years by introducing 'soapless', or detergent-free, soaps which provide all the refreshment, lather and cleansing power of ordinary soap with none of their abrasive alkaline content, and therefore drying and damaging effects on the skin.

These new cleansing bars and complexion soaps gently dissolve dirt and excess grease removing all remnants of make-up and dirt without stripping the skin's protective 'acid mantle' – the blend of natural oils and moisture that protects and conditions the complexion. Gentler still are water-soluble cleansing creams and lotions that liquify all traces of make-up and rinse off with warm water, leaving no oily residue. And what about the excessively dry skinned? Those women with a total aversion to the feel of water on the face can pick from a very broad range of cleansing milks, creams and lotions that whisk away make-up, dirt, and grease and are simply wiped off with tissues or cotton wool. If you use one of these cleansers make sure that you always remove all traces of lotion with a mild skin freshner or tonic.

Eye make-up, whether it is waterproof or not, is notoriously difficult to remove without leaving dark panda circles around the eyes. This is where it's worth investing in a specially formulated eye make-up remover which contains oils that dissolve mascara, eyeliner and shadow. Generally speaking, impregnated pads and clear liquid removers are ideal for removing non-waterproof eye make-up, but the heavier cosmetics respond more effectively to a thicker, oilier milk or lotion. Above all never rub, pull or stretch the delicate tissues around the eyes when cleansing – this is the quickest way to encourage lines, wrinkles, crêpeyness and crow's feet.

TONICS
fresh and gentle

Skin tonics or fresheners have today replaced the harsh astringents beauticians used to recommend for 'closing the pores' after cleansing. We know now that you cannot make pores close or even tighten up for more than about ten minutes, and while they may have a tingly, bracing effect, strong alcohol-based lotions can eventually coarsen and irritate the skin, creating surface dryness and broken viens. Gentle, alcohol-free tonics are far better for refreshing, stimulating and refining all skin types, while oily skins respond well to the natural astringent action of herbs like witch hazel or a cucumber-based tonic. Also very much in vogue these days is mineral water – the same sort you drink – in spray form. Though expensive, these sprays do actually have a very gentle and calming effect on all skins – even the very sensitive – and can be used repeatedly throughout the day. A good way to save money, however, is to decant an ordinary bottle of mineral water into a spray bottle – while lacking snob appeal the effect is exactly the same! For an added *frisson*, keep it stored in the fridge.

EXFOLIATION
giving nature a hand

Ever thought that lizards, who shed their skin regularly, might have cornered one of the world's beauty secrets? Dead cells, trapped waste matter, clogged make-up and general debris can all too easily build up on the skin's surface into a toughened barrier of old skin which prevents treatment creams from penetrating the epidermis and creates a lifeless, lined and grey-looking skin. Exfoliation, or surface peeling, is a messy but effective extension of deep cleansing, which, if used once or twice a week, will certainly refine, brighten and soften the complexion by sloughing off this dingy curtain.

Steaming the face over a bowl of boiling water, or a facial sauna, will help to loosen impurities, open the pores and

make it easier for exfoliating creams and lotions to work effectively. Suspended within these creams is a mass of microscopic granules, which will massage the epidermis, lift off dead surface skin, and refine and stimulate the layer beneath. Some exfoliators are designed to lather up and rinse off with water – use them with a soft complexion brush or a special facial 'loofah' pad to buff and polish a new glow onto the skin. Exfoliators are also particularly useful of course for softening and polishing up areas that are prone to collect patches of hard, dead skin such as elbows, heels and knees.

MASKS
for every occasion

Most complexions need 'revving up' at some time or another to stop them getting lethargic and sluggish, and there are few skins that don't improve from a weekly or fortnightly application of a face mask – a calculated revitalizer. Clay and other earth-based or seaweed-based 'mud packs' are ideal for oily, coarse, open-pored skins, while cleansing and tonifying peel-off masks are gentler and more suitable for refining and brightening drier skins. Masks that contain camphor, menthol and other stimulating ingredients wake up tired, stressed skin and are invaluable before a special night out. Thick gel or cream masks which don't harden are suitable for very dry or more mature skins and can often be used right up around the eye area since they are specifically formulated to nourish even fine tissue and erase lines of tension from the face. Apply your mask all over the neck area – this is a prime giveaway area as far as signs of neglect, dryness and premature ageing go – but remember also to always extend all your cleansing, exfoliating and moisturizing programmes right down to the collarbone to prevent crêpey, lined, dull neck tissue.

MOISTURE
the vital balance

Whatever your age, your moisturizer should qualify as the basic necessity you'd choose to accompany you on a desert island. Just imagine that the upper layer of your skin acts as a moisture trap, which, as water evaporates, is constantly replenished

The moisture level of skin is constantly being depleted by modern-day hazards such as central heating, air conditioning and pollution. It is crucial therefore to use a moisturizer to prevent dehydration, whatever type of skin you may have.

by fresh supplies generated within the deeper skin tissues. Depending on how much you expose your skin to the drying effects of the sun, harsh extremes of weather, central heating, air conditioning and pollution, these reserves gradually become depleted over the years. Furthermore this type of assault on our skin has risen to massive proportions over the past fifteen years. The result? The complexion of the eighties is more at risk: it gets drier and is more susceptible to tautness, lines, wrinkles, red veins, and patches of dehydration.

One moisturizer is by no means the same as another, whatever you may have heard. For instance, very fine, fluid moisturizing lotions are largely composed of water – often up to 80 per cent – and act principally by protecting your skin with an invisible, greaseless film that checks the evaporation of moisture from the skin. Such moisture lotions can contain a variety of humectants – natural moisturizing substances that help to attract moisture from the atmosphere into your skin. Known as oil-in-water emulsions these are ideal for protecting very young or oily skins, especially in humid weather. Richer, water-in-oil creams and lotions, however, contain a far greater percentage of oils, fats and waxes and so nourish and protect the skin more thoroughly, replacing as well as guarding moisture levels, plumping out tiny lines and wrinkles and covering the skin with a light occlusive barrier. The drier your skin – and the air around you – the harder and more efficiently your moisturizer needs to work. That doesn't mean you have to go in for heavy, clogging creams however. The manufacture and blending of emollients, water and humectants has today become a cosmetic art, and even the richest moisturizers are so refined that they're instantly absorbed leaving no tacky residue and allowing the smooth application of make-up.

NIGHT CARE
the lighter touch

Not so long ago the term night cream was synonymous with thick, gooey products that ruined romance and bedlinen, while doing precious little for the condition of your skin. Not any more. To be truly effective, any cream – whether worn at night or during the day – must be quickly and completely absorbed by the skin.

Actually it seems there's little difference now between a deep-acting night cream and a nourishing day cream – increasingly these are designed for use twenty-four hours a day, making life a lot simpler. Treatment creams are generally thicker and more emollient than regular moisturizers, usually working out at about 70 per cent oil and 30 per cent water. Cold cream and lanolin are good examples of the sort of consistency to expect – but you'll find more effective lightweight products on the market. They work mainly by softening the epidermis, preventing surface dehydration – though this is much less of a risk by night than during the day – and easing away lines of tension and expression that have become etched onto the face during the day. The aim behind the regular use of a night treatment cream is to stave off the formation of deeper wrinkles and creases. A word of caution however. There is no such thing as a rejuvenating cream or a miracle ingredient 'X' that can prevent normal expression lines from forming or which will keep your face forever set at twenty-two. Moreover, if you are indulging in late nights, drinking too much alcohol and coffee, chain smoking and getting no exercise, even the finest cream in the world will not hide the toll this takes on your skin and facial contours generally. There's no need to be lavish with night cream, that's another outmoded concept. Use it in small dots all over the face, massaging upwards and outwards without pulling the tissues. Areas that need careful attention are the neck, forehead and the skin around the mouth and the eyes. However, since the tissues around the eyes are paper thin, lacking in sebaceous glands, exceptionally delicate and liable to dehydration, it's best to care for this essential 'danger zone' with a specially refined eye cream. These are intended to feed extra nourishment into the tissues without overloading or stretching the skin. Use only a tiny dot at a time, pat in gently with your third finger, and make sure you blot off any excess or you'll wake up with puffy, congested eyes.

Oils in general tend to be too heavy for the skin of the face – they're best left for body conditioning. In exceptional cases, oils made from the pure distilled essences of plants can be used to treat very dehydrated, tired or mature skins. These must, however, be specially prescribed for your skin type by a trained therapist, and are intended to be combined with special massage techniques. If you do like the feel

of oil rather than cream on the skin, make sure you buy a pure, plant-based extract such as almond, apricot kernel, wheatgerm or avocado oil or pure vitamin E, and massage well into the skin using only a few drops at a time.

ENERGIZING
the newest concept

These's a lot of talk nowadays about skin energizing, using biologically active skin products. But how effective is this latest crop of treatment creams – if at all? Far from being yet another commercial gimmick aimed at luring us into spending money on our skin, they do in fact represent a very important breakthrough in cosmetic chemistry. Alternatively labelled 'energizing' or 'performance' creams, these have been especially developed to penetrate the epidermis, into those layers of tissue where cell activity is rife.

With the help of the latest technology, chemists claim that they can now analyse the essential active ingredients of young healthy skin as well as isolate those substances which are believed to play the most important role in bolstering cell activity and keeping the balance of moisture topped up. These creams aim to boost the quality and renewal rate of skin cells, which is absolutely vital to the maintenance of smooth, soft, young-looking skin. Special tests also indicate just how far into the epidermis these active substances can penetrate – which gives short shrift to those dermatologists who say that cosmetics cannot be absorbed by the skin. Yet far from relying on any new-found miracle ingredient, these products generally contain a complex variety of different substances to reduce the loss of moisture, slow down the destructive effects of pollution, protect the skin's collagen and elastic network fibres, and reduce the ill-effects of sunlight on the skin. Generally intended to be worn night and day beneath your usual moisturizer and nourishing cream, energizers often come in tiny phials, the contents used two or three drops at a time. Though it's too early to judge whether they can significantly slow down the march of time, they certainly have a beneficial, immediate effect on most skins, improving texture and tone, reducing existing lines and delaying the formation of new ones.

THE SUN
friend or foe?

Bronzed summer skin still rates undeniably high in the glamour stakes. It's a status symbol and instant cosmetic rolled into one devastatingly healthy, sexy look. It's something we save up for, travel the world for, and cultivate with endless patience. Instant appeal certainly – but in the long run, what's the true value of a tan?

We have all heard an increasing amount about the damaging effects of strong sunlight on the skin. Dermatologists keep warning us in no uncertain terms that ultraviolet light is the skin's arch-enemy – and unfortunately, at least for those of us who like to look tanned, they're absolutely right. Tan now, pay later is the message, for sun damage begins slowly and deep down within the base layers of the epidermis to surface only years later in the guise of blotchy, weathered, thinning, wrinkled and prematurely dehydrated skin. Repeated overexposure to strong sunlight is the most common cause of destruction of the skin's collagen and elastic fibres, speeding the formation of lines, wrinkles, and leading to a loss of elasticity. To be fair, however, doctors are most concerned about the fate of people with very fair skins who soak up the sun all the year round in countries such as Australia, South Africa and parts of America. The incidence of skin cancer is much greater in these countries than in other parts of the world and the reason for this is indiscriminate, long exposure to the sun. Most of us in Britain tend on average to sunbathe for two or three weeks a year and therefore the risk of serious skin damage is greatly reduced.

But what about those ageing effects? These of course *can* creep up on you if you don't take sufficient care of your skin in the sun at all times and allow it to burn. Ultraviolet light is made up of two principal types of rays: longwave UVA rays which produce a tan and rarely burn, and shortwave UVB rays which both burn *and* tan you. It's the burning UVB rays which are chiefly to blame for causing degenerative changes within the skin and unfortunately, the further south you venture for your holidays, the greater the intensity of these shortwave rays. While the risk of overexposure to UVB light increases steadily further south, it is of course just as possible to suffer severe sunburn while sitting in your back garden during a hot sunny July day in England! How your skin reacts now, as well as in the longterm, to repeated exposure to sunlight depends almost entirely on your skin type and its ability to build up a tan.

The reason why some people rapidly acquire a gorgeous golden tan while others turn red and peel depends entirely on a substance called melanin. Melanin is the skin pigment produced by skin cells which secrete and distribute extra quantities of pigment in the form of a tan when stimulated by UVA rays and some of the UVB rays. In some of us, melanin production increases with gradual exposure to the sun, acting as nature's own inbuilt defence against sunburn. People with black skins obviously have the greatest amount of melanin, while those of us with dark hair and sallow, olive skin usually tend to produce sufficient melanin to develop a dark or medium tan. Those at greatest risk from burning are people with very fair or red hair, pale delicate skin or freckled skin whose low quota of melanin-producing cells turns their skin into prime fuel for the sun's rays.

You must avoid burning, whatever your skin type. The skin's sensitivity changes with age and general health, so don't be caught off guard. Just because you have never suffered from sunburn doesn't guarantee permanent natural immunity. Bear in mind also that taking strong medicines like antibiotics, some tranquillizers and the pill can sometimes cause a skin reaction if you go into strong sunlight. The easiest time to burn in the sun is between eleven a.m. and three p.m. especially if cool sea breezes make you underestimate the power of the sun. You are also more liable to burn quickly if the sun's intensity is doubled through reflection off water, snow, concrete and even sand. Also, don't forget the 'delay factor'; sunburn can take anything from three to seven hours to appear, so don't be fooled if at first your skin seems to remain pallid in the sun – by evening it could well be kindled to a choice shade of lobster!

TO BURN OR NOT
the options

Nowadays everybody has the opportunity to tan safely and slowly without burning. Modern sunscreens really *do* cut out the most damaging wavelengths of strong sunlight while conditioning and moisturizing the skin, and more companies are perfecting very powerful screens and blocking agents that offer almost 100 per cent protection from the sun. Always apply sunscreens *before* going out into the sun and choose one that will give you adequate protection.

Most of today's leading brands carry what's called a *protection factor* (PF) which ranges from 2 to 16. Low numbers, from 2 to 4 or 5, are fine for dark skins that tan easily or for using when you are already tanned on the last few days of your holiday. A PF of 6, 7, 8 or more should be used at the start of the holiday, especially by people with very fair skins. In addition there are *total sun block* preparations that will give you complete protection from burning and also stop you going brown. These are ideal for vulnerable areas such as the nose, eyelids, lips or any part of you that gets a bit tender and pink.

To find the correct PF factor for your skin type, work out how long you can usually expose your skin to the sun before it starts to redden – then multiply this by the PF number of the sunscreen. So, if you start to go pink after 30 minutes, a sunscreen with a PF of 4 will protect you for up to two hours (i.e. 4 × 30 minutes). If you *do* burn you must of course stay out of the sun completely and treat your skin with a special healing lotion, calamine lotion, or best of all, natural yoghourt to take the pain out of the burn.

Some sunscreen products contain special tan accelerators which sensitize the skin to the sun and therefore encourage it to go brown slightly faster than it normally would. These accelerating agents or psoralens – such as bergamot oil – should be used with extreme caution. Some doctors have expressed the fear that they may cause skin cancer, but as they have only been in use for two or three years their long-term effects are not yet known. However, more certainly, instead of turning you an even brown, they can lead to blotchy tans which will take some time to fade. The use of these products while tanning on a sunbed is also potentially hazardous, because it can rapidly cause the formation of dark blotches which are extremely difficult to remove.

Lastly, no matter how hardy and resilient your skin seems to be right now, or how much you love a suntan, do try and think ahead a few years. Repeated overexposure to the sun will inevitably increase your chances of looking prematurely aged. You have only to compare the complexion of a woman of fifty who has never been in the sun to someone of the same age – or even five to ten years younger – who is a sun-worshipper to see that tanning rarely allows skin to age truly gracefully. Note those tell-tale areas of pigmentation, red veins, wrinkles, crow's feet, that might otherwise have been avoided, then ask yourself if that's a price worth paying for just a few weeks of bronzed glamour every year.

FAKING IT

You may have noticed of course that there are an increasing number of people around these days with beautiful suntans who've not set foot in sunny climes. Sunbeds, which tan you fast, simply and painlessly and wreak no visible havoc with the skin, offer a valid – if expensive – alternative to roasting oneself under the real thing. They work by bombarding the body with a very high concentration of pure UVA light so that you end up tanned and not burnt. However, it's worth remembering that as sunbeds are a relatively recent innovation, doctors cannot tell for sure at this stage whether their regular longterm use could prove harmful to the skin. Artificial UVA light is probably a great deal less damaging to skin in the long run than too much natural sunlight – provided you follow the rules. This means showering beforehand to remove all traces of perfume, oils, creams or cologne which could create an allergic reaction to the UVA light; using goggles to protect the eyes; and checking that you're not taking any medication that could make the skin extra sensitive.

Always go to a reputable suntan parlour or salon where the therapists are properly trained. Hygiene is an aspect of sunbed treatments that is too frequently overlooked in many salons around the country, so check that the beds are washed down between clients. You mustn't take UVA sun treatment if you are pregnant and you should leave forty-eight hours between

Before going out in the sun, it's vital to apply a sunscreen with a PF that suits your skin tone.

Very fair skin PF6 – 10

Fair skin PF5

Medium skin PF3 or 4

Dark or tanned skin PF2 or 3

each session. A course of tanning treatments can greatly help people with fair skins gain a headstart on acquiring a tan before going on holiday and help to maintain a healthy bronzed look long after they've returned.

SKIN PROBLEMS
getting a perspective

Nearly everyone is hypercritical of their own looks – to the point of excess. Ask someone with even an apparently flawless complexion how they'd rate their skin and they'll inevitably point out some blemish or flaw you'd need a microscope to find! Of course there *are* certain very common, often minor conditions that many of us must learn to live with, especially those that are inherited and largely irreversible, but in almost the majority of cases these really do appear much worse and more glaringly obvious to you than to anyone else. Try not to exaggerate their importance. There is after all no such phenomenon as a 100 per cent perfect complexion.

Sallow skin
often accompanies brunette hair, brown or dark eyes, and an olive or greasy complexion that tans easily. Unfortunately when you are not tanned it can look dingy and lack lustre. One big bonus, however, is that sallow skin is much less liable to suffer dehydration and develop early wrinkles than other skin types. Poor circulation is often a problem here so take lots of exercise, preferably out of doors. Treat your skin to regular steaming, stimulating masks and exfoliation and use a facial washing brush to keep spots and blackheads at bay.

Lines and wrinkles
that appear prematurely are often the spin off from too much sunbathing, harsh weather, dry atmospheres, smoking or losing a lot of weight very suddenly. A certain number of expression lines are only to be expected from the mid-twenties on – due as much to our personalities and the faces we pull when we smile, talk, laugh and frown as to lack of skin care. Using a good protective moisturizer and night cream daily, however, will go some way towards delaying the formation of premature lines and deep wrinkles as we grow older.

Red veins
tend to appear more noticeable on very delicate, dry skin and one that reacts adversely to extremes of hot and cold. So treat the skin gently and avoid drinking very hot liquids, eating very hot or spicy food and go easy on saunas, steaming and sunbathing. Severe broken veins can be treated by sclerotherapy, a specialized injection using a chemical fluid whereby the traces of blood are dried out so that they fade away and the broken capillary wall is sealed off. Milder or superficial capillaries can be treated by electrolysis which cauterizes each capillary. There's little you can do to cool down a ruddy or flushed complexion except to use soothing decongesting creams and gels and a make-up shade that tones down high colour.

Surplus hair
may become an added problem during hormonal changes or as a result of taking the pill and can sometimes increase with age. Light down on the upper lip can quite safely be bleached to make it appear less noticeable, however, never pluck, shave or even wax facial hair. Electrolysis is the only way to remove hair permanently, and is painless and 100 per cent effective if practised by a qualified therapist.

Open pores
also tend to be a by-product of greasy skin. There's little you can do to shrink them, just cleanse, exfoliate and refine with a mask or mud astringent to combat blackheads and spots. Use an oil-free foundation make-up base to minimize the appearance of large pores and to prevent them clogging and therefore appearing worse.

Blackheads
are not, as often supposed, trapped dirt, but the direct result of oxygen coming into contact with trapped sebum. This is why they are often a problem for people with oily skin and coarse enlarged pores, especially around the nose and chin. Scrupulous cleansing, exfoliation, face masks and the regular use of a facial washing brush will refine open pores and prevent oil from settling, while also softening and easing out any existing blackheads. Never attempt to remove blackheads yourself at home by prodding or squeezing them, as this could lead to permanent scarring. Consult a trained beautician if you want them removed correctly.

An occasional spot is almost unavoidable. Take care however to treat it quickly or others may follow.

Moles

are nothing to worry about provided they don't change shape, grow dramatically or bleed. Don't try to remove hairs if they are growing out of a mole. Avoid salon treatments and consult a dermatologist if you want a mole checked or removed.

Spots and pimples

There can be virtually nobody who does not at sometime or other in their lives suffer from the occasional 'breakout' of spots either during a period, as a result of changes in the weather, using different skincare products or just plain stress and tension. The odd spot – as opposed to acne – is nothing to worry about provided you deal with it promptly to avoid cross-infection. This means meticulously cleaning the spot area, preferably with a medicated wash-off lotion to whisk away grime and bacteria, and using a medicated cream, lotion, or gel to disinfect and dry out the offending area as quickly as possible. There are some excellent deep-acting antiseptic agents on the market which make short shrift of pimples. They are generally very drying to the skin however, so be careful not to use them too often if you have a very sensitive or dry skin. A course of Brewer's Yeast, rich in the B complex vitamins, can also work wonders in helping to clear a spotty skin. (For advice on treating acne, see p. 72).

Milia

or whiteheads are spots of trapped oil just beneath the skin's surface and show up as tiny hard bumps about the size of a pinhead – usually around the eye socket, cheekbones and generally on bony areas where there are fewer pores to allow sebum to escape. They can often result from warm weather or a change in diet and disappear later on. You can usually banish them in a few weeks with a mild antiseptic lotion.

Freckles

go with fair skins, auburn, fair or red hair and become more pronounced in the summer, multiplying especially if you go into the sun. Bleaching creams have little effect on them, so avoid the sun if you want an even complexion and choose a foundation with extra coverage to hide them completely.

Brown patches

(chloasma) can appear while you are pregnant or after sunbathing if you are on the pill. The higher levels of female hormones in the body at this time sometimes make certain parts of the face extra sensitive to sunlight so that they come up in dark brown, muddy-looking blotches especially around the eyes, on the upper lip, across the forehead and on the cheeks. Unfortunately there's little you can do to stop them recurring, except avoid the sun or come off the pill during the summer. Try using a hydroquinone-based bleaching cream for eight to ten weeks – this can often eliminate the patches quite effectively. Alternatively, a dermatologist might be able to prescribe a much stronger bleaching agent for you. A small percentage of women, however, find that their skin becomes red and ultra-sensitive to these creams, especially during very cold weather. Once you've successfully bleached away the dark areas, make sure you wear a strong sun block over them when you go into the sun to stop the blotches intensifying once again.

Allergic skin

is often confused with very fragile, delicate skin that gets easily irritated. True allergy-prone skin is a much rarer condition and is often linked to a family history of hay fever, asthma and migraine. Tracking down the offending substance to which you are allergic is of course the hardest part of solving the problem – but well worth the trouble in the long run. Your doctor or skin specialist can help you greatly with this and will probably ask you to make lists of foods, cosmetics, household and other common products that you use. Obviously if you tend to develop an allergic reaction to some cosmetics you must always try out new products with a patch test in the crook of your arm and wait twenty-four hours to see if they suit you.

Rosacea

is often confused with allergic skin since this is a skin that becomes sensitive and reacts violently to changes of atmosphere, sunlight, hot food and drink, becoming ruddy and developing a mass of tiny red spots. It tends to affect people whose temperament makes them excessively prone to nervous tension and stress and occasionally those who have suffered from acute acne. Doctors often prescribe a course of antibiotics to calm down the condition and it is a good idea to use skincare products that have a cooling effect as well as camouflaging make-up to mask the redness.

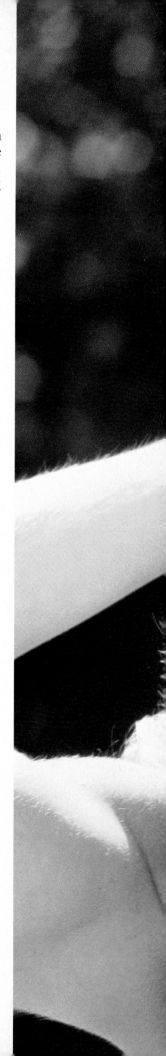

HANDS, LEGS, FEET AND TEETH

FOCUS ON HANDS AND NAILS

Instantly eye catching, totally expressive, our hands are frequently overlooked, even abused, says hand and nail expert Jacqueline Burgess Wall, who runs a London beauty studio specialising in the care of hands and nails. Considering the onslaught of water, detergents, weathering and grime we subject our hands to, they should merit the most devoted, well-thought out of all beauty routines: too often, however, they tend instead to be one of the earliest and cruellest giveaways of age, accumulating marks of time that after a certain age are extremely difficult to erase. Yet all of this could be avoided provided we all followed a few simple home rules. Gloves are undoubtedly one of the finest beauty aids. The more sensitive and dry the skin on the backs of your hands the more important it is to remember to wear rubber gloves whenever you immerse them in detergent. Cotton-lined rubber gloves are a good idea if your skin is very sensitive, as they are more comfortable and less likely to cause irritation. These will cut out about 70 per cent of the main causes of dehydration. The reason why our hands dry out so quickly and easily is that there are no sebaceous glands to keep them supple.

Wear cotton gloves when gardening and doing housework and leather or woolly ones in cold weather. Each time you wash your hands, massage plenty of rich hand cream into the tissues and never wash your hands in very hot water. Barrier creams contain a particularly high concentration of protective ingredients like silicone which provide more intensive and long-lasting protection against water and detergents. Warm olive oil is ideal for coaxing the moisture back into dry hands; soak them thoroughly for half an hour every week to treat splitting nails, and to condition the skin and cuticles. To bleach out stubborn stains and yellowish discolouration rub them with half a lemon. There's unfortunately very little you can do to get rid of the brown 'liver spots' which sometimes appear in middle age. No one knows what actually causes them, though they are possibly due to a malfunction in the pigment cells and almost definitely linked to frequent and prolonged sunbathing.

NAILS– the big challenge

Beautifully long, strong nails need patient cultivation and a certain amount of know-how. The reason why so many women suffer from weak, splitting, peeling or brittle nails is quite simply because they are unaware of how easy it is to inflict damage on and around the nail itself. The visible portion of the nail, just like the skin's surface and our hair, is made up of tightly compressed dead cells that have grown out of the living nail bed – the matrix – which is rich in blood capillaries and nerve endings that nourish the nail tissue. The condition of your nails therefore is a pretty accurate reflection of your general health including the medicines you take, your diet and stress levels. Prolonged illness or emotional shocks, for instance, can show up in ridged, thin, weak nails; a problem that only becomes noticeable sometime after the event because nails take anything from four to nine months to grow out fully. Your nails will also tend to reflect dietary deficiencies in protein, vitamins A and B complex, iron, magnesium, zinc and calcium.

As long as your health and eating habits are well balanced there is certainly plenty you can do to build up strong healthy nails from outside. Use cuticle cream regularly to nourish and soften the cuticles as the tissue is fundamental in protecting the smoothness and strength of new nail growth. Never jab, prod, push or cut the cuticles with a sharp object and steer clear of dissolvent creams as these only coarsen the skin and make it look messier. It is important to keep the cuticle pliable and free of the actual nail plate, otherwise it impedes unrestricted growth and causes marks or indentations. Excessive acidity, which generally stems from diet, is one of the most common causes of vertical or horizontal ridges, splitting and breaking nails. Furthermore, if acid collects on the surface of the nail along with the body's

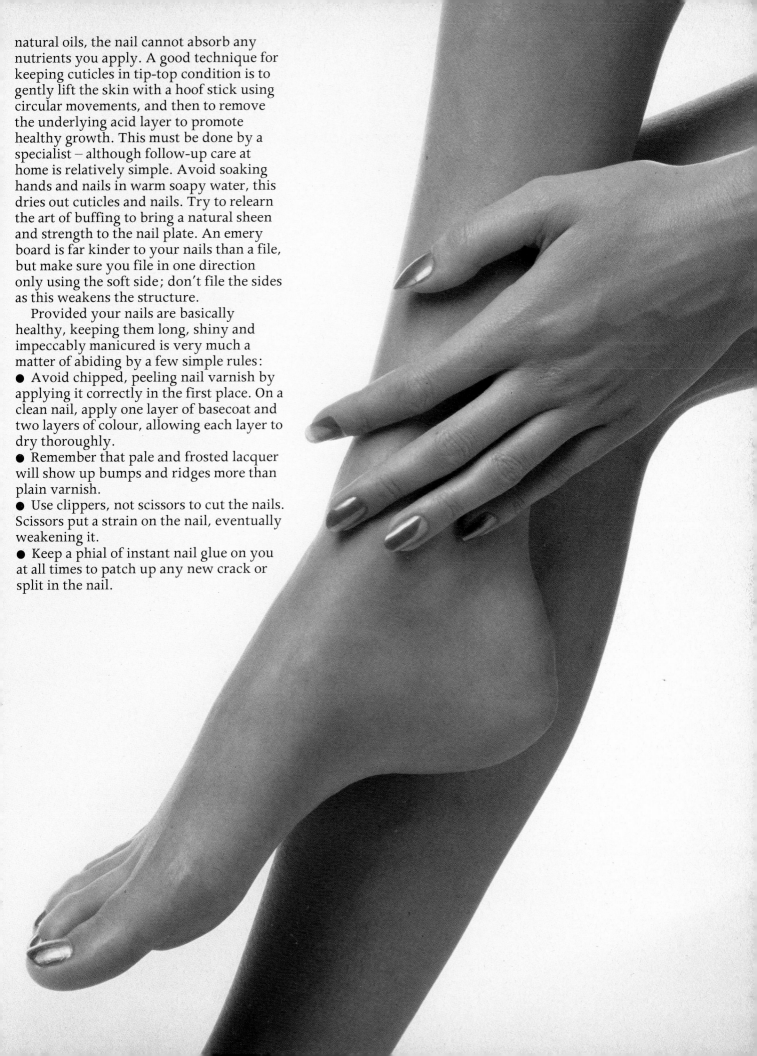

natural oils, the nail cannot absorb any nutrients you apply. A good technique for keeping cuticles in tip-top condition is to gently lift the skin with a hoof stick using circular movements, and then to remove the underlying acid layer to promote healthy growth. This must be done by a specialist – although follow-up care at home is relatively simple. Avoid soaking hands and nails in warm soapy water, this dries out cuticles and nails. Try to relearn the art of buffing to bring a natural sheen and strength to the nail plate. An emery board is far kinder to your nails than a file, but make sure you file in one direction only using the soft side; don't file the sides as this weakens the structure.

Provided your nails are basically healthy, keeping them long, shiny and impeccably manicured is very much a matter of abiding by a few simple rules:

● Avoid chipped, peeling nail varnish by applying it correctly in the first place. On a clean nail, apply one layer of basecoat and two layers of colour, allowing each layer to dry thoroughly.

● Remember that pale and frosted lacquer will show up bumps and ridges more than plain varnish.

● Use clippers, not scissors to cut the nails. Scissors put a strain on the nail, eventually weakening it.

● Keep a phial of instant nail glue on you at all times to patch up any new crack or split in the nail.

● Steer clear of artificial nail-building techniques or false nails generally. These involve the use of very powerful chemicals which not only weaken and wear down the remnants of your own nails but can also cause fungus infections and a risk of allergies.

● To slim down the appearance of broad, flat nails, apply a strong shade of nail lacquer down the centre of the nail leaving a narrow unpainted strip on either side.

● Always use nail varnish remover that contains oil. Cheaper, oil-free brands dry out the nail and cuticle.

● To strengthen nails, opt for regular use of a really top quality cuticle oil or cream rather than a nail hardener which only treats the tips of the nails.

● Ridges are often caused through damaging the nail bed or cuticle, so take care not to treat them roughly. Ridges can be filled in with special preparations (though these have a drying effect), treated at a salon, or smoothed away with buffing.

● Scrubbing the nails with a hard brush can cause them to separate from the nail bed and so weaken them. Clean instead with a cuticle stick or a special nail sponge.

LEGS
tops in the glamour stakes

For instant sex appeal and glamour there's little to beat a long slinky pair of legs. If you want to know how yours rate, stand in front of a full-length mirror, wearing medium heeled shoes, feet together. Do your legs touch at the tops of the thighs, knees and ankles, leaving three gently curved gaps between each point of contact? If so, your legs are well on the way to model-girl proportions. Legs should be lean and lithe, not sticklike and skinny – and certainly not covered in bulges and bumps. Massage and exercise rather than dieting are the greatest leg shapers. Watch out for common pitfalls that may mar a shapely leg:

Varicose veins
are a circulatory complaint which is often hereditary and can occur even at an early age. Warning signs are cramp, irritation

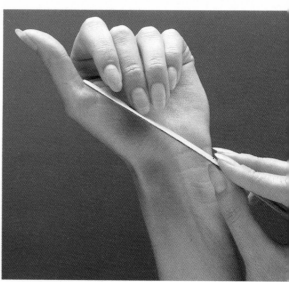

Above left. Apply instant nail glue to cracks and splits. **Above right.** File the nail with the soft side of the emery board. **Below left.** Gently lift the cuticle free of the nail plate with a hoof stick. **Below right.** Use a buffer to polish and strengthen the nails

burning, swelling of the leg beneath the knee and throbbing, clearly defined veins. Avoid standing around for long periods, don't wear tight socks or stockings, try not to cross your legs while you sit, and never jog or exercise on hard surfaces like concrete. Put your feet up whenever you can and wear fashionable lightweight support tights. Also try to switch heel heights during the day and massage your legs with a cooling gel or cream to get the circulation going. Being pregnant, overweight or prone to constipation can make varicose veins worse. If yours are particularly severe you can have injections to treat them or an operation to remove them completely.

Water retention and swelling

are also a sign of poor circulation and may be a special problem just before menstruation when the body tends to retain fluid. Wear support tights to protect against the risk of varicose veins, don't stand in one spot for long periods and put your feet up when you can. Make sure you drink enough water to eliminate waste products from the system. Eating less salt can help to combat water retention, but if the root cause is hormonal imbalance your doctor may have to treat this.

Cellulite

can mar even the slenderest of legs. Hard, slightly pitted flesh and lumps and bulges on the upper thighs and buttocks, which won't go away even when you lose weight, are generally caused through fluid retention and an accumulation of toxic waste in the tissue. Regular massage with a rough bath mitt or hemp glove and a special ivy- or seaweed-based cream can work wonders in decongesting and breaking down these fatty deposits. Also try to eliminate most of the salt and spices in your diet and drink at least six to eight glasses of water or herb tea a day. The best exercises to shape up and firm the thighs are swimming, fast walking, dancing and gym exercises.

Surplus hair

can be removed in a variety of ways. If you like a 'wet' shave, always use a sharp blade and wield it slowly and steadily to avoid nicks and cuts. Coat the legs with a fine layer of talcum powder if you use an electric shaver and lavish plenty of body conditioner onto the legs after shaving. Depilatory creams and lotions tend to give you a smoother, more silky finish, while

waxing rates as far the most superior method as it removes hairs at the root so that they grow back over a longer period of time. Waxing is relatively expensive (home kits are messy, difficult to use and a waste of money), but where you score is that regrowth is usually finer than after regular shaving or depilation, which makes it ideal for the summer months when bare legs usually go on show. It is worth remembering, however, that provided you follow the rules you cannot damage your legs or skin through shaving, nor will you stimulate the growth of hair.

SPOTLIGHT ON FEET

Most of us are born with perfect feet – yet nine out of ten people develop foot problems of one kind or another before they reach the age of twenty. The majority of these occur when the correct balance of the foot is misplaced. Through wearing ill-fitting shoes and walking incorrectly the muscles and arches become weakened and the ligaments overstretched, creating excessive pressure on parts of the foot. This friction can lead to the formation of callouses, corns, and more serious conditions such as enlarged toe joints and bunions. Ignore these early warning signs at your peril! Supremely eloquent, your feet speak volumes on your general well-being. For, as we all know, foot problems are not confined locally but tend to lead to back problems, aching legs, headaches and general ill-temper! Yet damage to the feet is by and large self-inflicted, through such passing whims of fashion as platform soles, very high heels or stillettos, which thrust the weight forward onto the ball of the foot, and tight, narrow or pointed toes that crunch up the toes into a vice-like grip. This is one case where it's certainly not worth considering the short-term advantages of fashion trends over long-term health and comfort. When you buy shoes therefore, bear in mind a few cardinal rules:
● A well-fitting shoe should be half an inch longer than your foot, allowing plenty of room to wriggle your toes around.
● Shoes must fit perfectly round the heels.
● They must give firm support to the arches.
● They mustn't pinch, rub or squeeze any part of the foot. Don't expect new shoes to 'give' with wear. They probably won't.
● Avoid synthetic fibres which 'draw' the feet making them sweat and swell in all weather. Choose soft leather or fabric.

FOOTNOTES

Socks, tights and stockings must also fit well, allowing room for movement. If they are tight and restricting they can be just as damaging as ill-fitting shoes. Regular elimination of rough skin with a pumice stone helps to avoid the formation of callouses. If the dreaded corns appear you must go to a chiropodist for treatment before they become a more agonising, deep-rooted problem. Felt pads, plasters and 'buffer' sponges can minimize the pressure of shoes and protect tender spots, and walking barefoot or wearing exercise sandals whenever possible helps to encourage mobility of the joints and relieve muscle tension and cramp. Your chiropodist can give you special exercises to attempt to straighten out the big toe if you think you may be developing a bunion. Once very large, inflamed and painful bunions have developed you may need to have an operation to remove them in order to make walking less of an agony.

Verrucae (a form of wart) and athlete's foot are both fungus infections that need immediate attention. Both are highly contagious conditions which flourish in warm, moist unhygienic surroundings – particularly in crowded areas like swimming pools or public changing rooms – and can be passed on by clothing, socks and towels. Verrucae must be professionally removed to prevent them growing or multiplying. If you notice the skin between the toes splitting, peeling or developing a rash (athlete's foot), bathe frequently and use an anti-fungal powder or spray on your feet and inside socks and shoes. There are special athlete's foot tinctures which will clear up the infection in a few weeks.

Ingrowing toenails, usually caused by cutting the nail too low at the corners and wearing ill-fitting shoes, must also be treated by a chiropodist before they dig deeper into the nail bed. Swollen, perspiring, throbbing feet and ankles are something all of us suffer from at one time or another, especially during hot summer months. Regular bathing, powdering and a cooling foot-refresher spray help to take a lot of the daily punishment out of walking on city pavements. If your feet really feel they've walked their final step, steep them in hot Epsom salts or splash them alternately with cold and warm water about twenty times to reduce puffiness.

Like feet, elbows also need regular softening with a loofah, body brush or buffing pad in order to skim off accumulated dead skin and prevent chafing from woolly sweaters. Keep them silky soft by massaging body lotion or hand cream into the skin after your bath.

STAYING FRESH

There's nothing unduly offensive about human sweat. Perspiring is one of the most natural – and important – bodily functions, acting as an inbuilt cooling system. Body odour, however, is most definitely unattractive, especially as it is controllable once you have found the products and daily routine that are effective for you. Choosing from the many different brands of anti-perspirants and deodorants on the market is largely a matter of finding what feels – and works – best for your own body. Generally speaking, people who perspire freely need an anti-perspirant that is labelled 'extra dry' or contains an extra strong long-lasting formula to restrict the flow of sweat. Roll-ons have more staying power than aerosols since they have a definite sealing action. Aerosol products, however, often contain powder, and therefore will make you feel fresher when you first apply them – but they usually need re-application in warm atmospheres. Remember, unless the instructions state otherwise, you must apply the product regularly each day after washing or bathing. To keep the underarms smooth and free of unwanted hair either try salon waxing, a depilatory cream, wet or electric shaving. Wait eight to ten hours before putting on anti-perspirant to avoid stinging or irritation. Dust underarms with baby powder to calm the skin if it's red and raw.

When the weather gets hot you'll probably feel like taking more baths and showers, but make sure they are not too hot or they won't have the desired cooling effect. To keep cool and fresh for longer try spraying the body with a scented spray or *eau de cologne*. Clammy hands are harder to control, but regular splashing with cool water and spraying with a mild anti-perspirant, body spray or cologne can help to keep them dry and cool. Winter or summer you will find you perspire far less if you avoid wearing synthetic fibres. Wear cotton, pure wool, linen against your skin, especially during warmer weather, and make sure you buy panties that are pure cotton – particularly the gusset area.

To banish plaque and food particles, and to strengthen gum tissue, brush at least twice a day with small, circular movements.

TEETH AND GUMS
avoiding trouble

It's a paradox that while women – and men – will spend time, money and a lot of effort on personal freshness, general grooming and every aspect of their outer appearance, oral health and hygiene by comparison qualifies as the poor relation! Yet strong, healthy, sparkling teeth and firm, well-shaped gums are surely an integral part of everyone's appearance, projecting charm and verve every time we smile or laugh. The reason why tooth decay is a national malady in so many western countries – and in Britain in particular – is that we eat an abundance of sugar and sweet food, especially between meals, and do not brush our teeth regularly or effectively enough to undo the subsequent damage. Caring for teeth and gums begins in very early childhood and is in fact a relatively painless, uncomplicated routine:

● Avoid eating sweets, chocolates, biscuits and chewing gum between meals. Sugar rapidly combines with the bacteria found in saliva to form acids which systematically weaken and erode your teeth. If you *do* eat something sweet, brush your teeth as soon as possible afterwards.

● Brush both teeth *and* gums correctly.

Hold the brush at an angle against the point where the teeth meet the gums and wiggle it against the surface with tiny circular movements. Concentrate on tiny areas at a time, resist large sweeping movements and brushstrokes and make sure you cover the outside, inside, sides and biting surfaces of the teeth.

● Learn to trace every last vestige of plaque. Plaque is the villain of teeth and gums. It is made up of a fine sticky film consisting of bacteria and saliva which adheres to nooks and crannies like gum margins, biting surfaces, and between the teeth. Plaque combines with particles of food – sugar in particular – to form acids, and unless it's promptly removed this lethal combination eats away at the surface of the tooth and causes decay. Since it's difficult to be sure you've banished every vestige of plaque, use a disclosing tablet (available from chemists) which dyes plaque red or blue so you can trace and brush it off completely. Use these tablets twice or three times a week.

● Add dental floss and gum massages to your dental 'kit'. They remove plaque and tiny bits of food from between the teeth and help to strengthen gums.

● Use a medium or soft toothbrush and change it every three months. Always buy toothpaste with added fluoride as this helps to strengthen the resistance of your teeth against the acids that cause decay.

● Take time to brush teeth properly. Ideally you should clean them after every meal – but few of us have sufficient time or opportunity. Never skimp brushing before bedtime, for most of the damage caused by food particles and acid build-up occurs while you are asleep. One five-minute assault a day, plus one or two slightly shorter brushing sessions should protect against tooth decay and weak gums.

● Gums are every bit as precious as teeth themselves. Watch out for bleeding while you brush as well as swelling or pocketing of the gum tissue which causes a tiny gap to form between the tooth and edge of the gum. These are signs that the gums are not sealing firmly against the tooth and therefore allowing plaque to filter through between the gums and teeth roots. If this hidden damage continues for too long, eventually the bone which holds the root will be eaten away, loosening the teeth. This is the main reason why so many people over the age of thirty-five have their teeth extracted. Correct brushing and flossing will help to prevent your gums from weakening.

HAIR-DOWN TO BASICS

The condition and style of your hair can have a devastating effect not only on your general appearance, but also on your self-confidence and inner feeling of well-being. On a bad day the state of your hair can do as much to depress you and make you feel an unkempt mess, as on another it can make you feel glamorous and elated.

After all there are few things more demoralizing than being caught out on a last minute social event or business appointment with hair that's lost its style or needs a wash or trim. Ultimately, says Daniel Galvin, mastermind behind one of London's most fashionable and respected treatment and colouring salons, our looks are judged by the quality and style of our hair. Fashionable clothes, jewellery, pretty make-up and chic accessories lose 80 per cent of their impact if they are teamed with hair that's either in poor condition or badly styled. Over the past ten or fifteen years, there has of course been a phenomenal revolution both in hair-care and styling, which has liberated us from gimmicky and elaborate hard-to-manage 'set' hairstyles and given more women the opportunity to state their individuality through the different ways in which they wear their hair. Almost any hairstyle is acceptable nowadays, as long as it suits your features, and never before has so much expert help been available when tackling hair and scalp problems or for altering the texture, colour and condition of hair itself.

HAIR TYPES

The texture and behaviour of hair (just like skin) determines both the way you need to treat it and how best to wear it. Since hair-care manufacturers nowadays produce special formulas for many different types of hair, it's important to identify yours.

Normal hair
– unfortunately rare – is usually delightfully well-behaved, neither too dry nor too greasy. The effects of washing and styling may last anything between five and eight days. Whether straight or curly, it is easy to manage, and adapts to a selection of diverse styles. Try not to perm or colour it as you may encourage problems.

Dry hair
generally goes with a dry scalp which doesn't produce enough natural oils to keep the surface of the hair soft, smooth and shiny. Often rather fine and flyaway, it tends to lack lustre and reacts badly to perming, tinting and extreme heat. Prone to split ends and breaking, conditioning is all important to feed the scalp and moisturize the outer cuticle of the hair.

Greasy hair
usually becomes lank, dull and dandruff-prone and loses its shape and bounce even a day or two after washing. Like an oily skin (which it often accompanies) it is due

Perfectly conditioned, impeccably cut, well-styled hair. The way you wear yours can have a devastating effect on your looks—and mood.

to overactive sebaceous glands (on the scalp) that coat the hair with an abundance of natural oils. Mild and frequent shampooing and a correct diet can help check oiliness.

Flyaway hair

is notoriously difficult to hold in certain styles since it often combines dryness with a lot of static electricity. Correct conditioning and use of blow-dry or setting lotions can tame the hair and make it more manageable.

Fine hair

is generally fair, often sparse and also reacts temperamentally to setting. Perming helps tremendously to add body. On the whole it's better to stick to natural, easy to manage styles which accentuate the sheen and texture of the hair.

Coarse hair

usually contains a lot of very dark pigment, is thick and easy to control and suits almost any style. If it's very straight and on the long side, however, the weight may pull against the effects of waving and curling. Dramatic or ultra-simple styles tend to suit coarse hair best.

Frizzy hair

is usually on the dry and flyaway side and can look coarse because of its lack of shine. It needs adequate conditioning and styling to coax more softness and order into the overall shape.

Straight hair

looks best worn in a simple style that shows off shine and texture. Looks good at any length but more than any other type of hair needs regular, impeccable cutting.

SHAMPOOS

'Conditioning comes before everything, after that comes the cut, then the colour. But if you don't have hair that's in perfect condition the last two don't mean a thing.' Strong words, but ones that underline today's all-out emphasis on an unstructured beauty that radiates health and fitness. Conditioning, more than a mere after-thought, begins the moment you wash your hair. These days this is a more subtle procedure than just shampooing up a storm of bubbles. To begin with, resist the urge to pick up any old jumbo-sized brand of cheap shampoo that catches your eye amongst the washing powders and scouring agents at the supermarket. Invest instead in protein-enriched, pH-balanced shampoos which cleanse hair and scalp gently instead of stripping them abrasively of oils and moisture.

Frequent shampooing with a harsh alkaline detergent product is the fastest way to loosen and rough up the outer scaly layer of your hair – the 'cuticle' – encouraging split ends and general dryness. Because all hair – whatever it's type – needs the tender touch, one really good shampoo can be used for every hair type. Just increase or decrease the frequency of washing, as well as the application, and work up less lather if you have greasy hair.

Resist the urge to let your hair wallow in suds; the more often you wash it, the more you should try and get by on only one application of shampoo – which is ample to dissolve and lift out grease, grime and general debris. However, if you suffer from a severely greasy scalp – with or without the added bane of dandruff – opt for a shampoo designed especially to combat and control the problem.

The way you treat your hair when it's wet also has lasting effects on it's general condition. More damage is inflicted to hair through rough, hasty, slipshod towelling and combing prior to drying, than during actual styling. It's a pitfall you can come up against, even at an established and leading hairdresser, if the shampoo girl or boy happens to have climbed out of the wrong side of bed on a particular day! Squeeze and pat water out of your hair – don't rub it endlessly with a rough towel, and never use a brush or a cheap, spikey, fine-toothed comb on wet hair. Hair is at its most elastic, and therefore its weakest, when wet, so gently ease out irritating knots and tangles with a broad-toothed comb with round edges. If your hair is long, begin combing slowly at the bottom of the hair and work your way upwards to reduce stress on the hair fibres.

CONDITIONING

Just as you wouldn't cleanse and wash your face without protecting it afterwards with a moisturizer, you shouldn't ask for hair problems by skipping on conditioning and retexturizing. Must like skincare products, conditioners work on different levels of the hair structure, depending on its degree of dryness and damage.

Instant *Creme Rinses*, fast and easy to use, act principally on the surface of the hair, coating it with a fine wax-like film that smooths down the ruffled scales of the outer cuticle helping to make hair shiny as well as manageable, tangle-free and more able to hold its style. Protein *Retexturizing Creams* and *Moisturizing Treatments* should be left on the hair for ten to twenty minutes as they help to correct damage caused by tinting, perming, bleaching, sunlight, central heating, seawater and chlorine as well as surface dehydration from hairdryers, tongs and heated rollers. They help to boost and strengthen the protein structure of damaged hair and should be used by anyone worried about brittle dry hair. Watch out for deeply nourishing and moisturizing elements like avocado, peachnut oil, eggs, honey, camomile, henna, coconut oil, lemon, nettle and rosemary. All are renowned for restoring suppleness to hair of all types. *Treatment packs* are much thicker, creamier products, rich in extra oils, waxes and other emollients. Like a face pack they must be kept on the hair for thirty minutes or more, depending on the amount of abuse that has been meted out to your hair in the cause of fickleness and fashion! Anyone with tinted, bleached, permed, or continually tonged and heated hair needs to redress as many of the ill-effects as possible by applying monthly or even weekly packs. As the head is usually covered with a polythene hood or a towel to trap body heat and make the oils penetrate more deeply, there are plenty of things you can be getting on with in the home while your hair is being treated. Even applying warm olive or almond oil to the scalp and massaging it in well and wrapping it in warm towels can help to

Even mild shampoos affect hair adversely in some way, so take care not to overshampoo with harsh drying products that will damage the hair cuticle.

recondition dry, brittle hair. Very fine, extra dry or flyaway hair may need coaxing into order and style with a *Hair Thickener* or a *Blow-dry Lotion* which is not rinsed off. These merely bond with the hair's outer layer, providing an added protective coating which builds body and strength, adds shine, and protects hair from overcooking under the heat of the hairdryer. Blow-dry lotions are an excellent safeguard against damage if your style requires a lot of tugging, brushing and tweaking while you dry it.

SHAPING UP
setting, drying and styling

Women tend to forget the immense strain on the hair imposed by regular shampooing, setting and drying. Hair cannot handle even very mild and gentle shampooing without reacting adversely in some way – however small.

When you are drying hair the most important thing to remember is to keep the air warm, never hot. Hair after all burns as much, if not as dramatically, as skin.

Roller setting is pretty passé as far as today's free and easy unstructured styles go, as any leading hairdresser will vouch; towel and finger drying, the use of hairdryers and allowing the hair to dry naturally are all less aggressive ways of putting shape and movement into hair.

However, if you are determined to achieve a neatly 'set' look – or else if you have very long or thick hair – try and follow a few basic rules to achieve a professional effect with the minimum amount of damage.

1. Sprinkle damp hair with setting lotion that contains the very minimum of alcohol.
2. Section off small areas of hair with precise partings and the help of a tail comb. Roll these very carefully and not too tightly beginning at the crown, working towards the front and sides and then the back. Never put too much tension on the hair and avoid spiked rollers which can damage the hair and cause splitting and breaking.
3. When hair is completely dry, remove rollers gently and brush hair thoroughly in one direction, then the other to eliminate any roller or pin marks.

Top left. Hold the dryer about six inches from the hair and keep it moving.

Top right. Begin by drying underneath the hair at the sides and the back of the head.

Below left. Lift the base of each section and dry each side thoroughly.

Below right. Lastly, guide the style in the direction you wish, but never concentrate the heat on the hair for too long.

Fuller, bouncy or curlier styles can be blow dried using a circular jumbo brush. Wrap each section securely around the brush and run warm air along all sides until the curl has taken. Add height by lifting and drying the underneath of each section first.

BLOW DRYING

A good brush, an accurate eye and a deft wrist are all you need to create some of the most bouncy, smooth and natural-looking styles. Good blow drying gives long-lasting shape and volume to medium and long hair and is invaluable for adding swing and movement to hair of any length, plus giving that jaunty lift at the roots that stops hair looking flat and lank.

1 Blot hair dry with a towel, comb gently and apply blow-dry lotion if you hair is fine or prone to static electricity.
2 Hold dryer at least six inches from the hair and keep it moving. To begin with ruffle the hair gently at the roots with the fingers to take out the dampness, then start to lift the base of different sections with your brush, drying the underneath of each section thoroughly.
3 To achieve last minute flicks or curves or to guide the style in a definite direction, wind sections of hair firmly over a round brush and direct the heat along the top of this for a moment or two, then unwind. Never 'grill' the hair.
4 Short, layered urchin cuts can be blow dried using just the finger to tweak and ruffle the hair casually into shape.

The size, shape and quality of the hairbrush you use is all important both to the condition as well as to the final result you want to achieve. Natural bristles are the gentlest, and ideal for very fine or frizzy hair, while nylon and bristle mixtures can be used on hair that's a bit thicker and coarser. Very long hair needs the support and even curve of a circular 'jumbo' brush, although it's easier to get under and around shorter, layered hair with a semi-circular brush or one that's round but has a small circumference. Straight-as-a-die styles fall more evenly and fully if trained into place with a broad flat brush, preferably one shaped to the head with bristles set into a rubber cushion. Remember also to always keep brushes and combs immaculately clean.

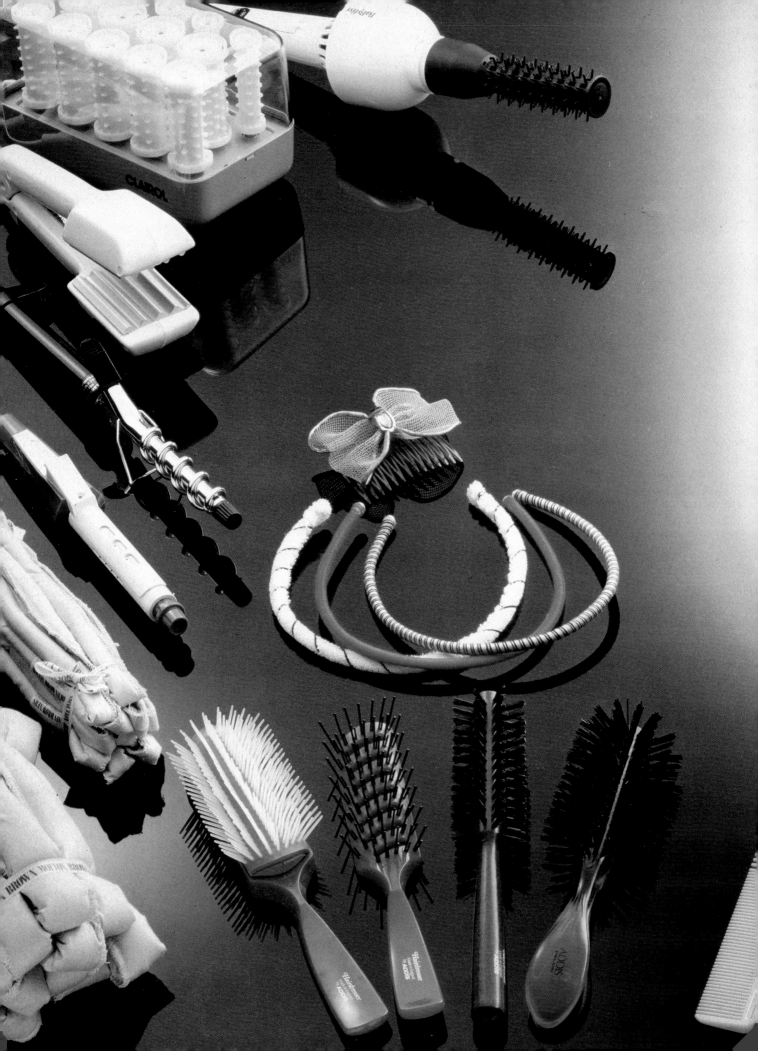

USEFUL APPLIANCES

In recent years, technology has taken a lot of the fuss and tedium out of hairstyling. As styles become freer and more versatile, so is today's hair gadgetry the more effective and easier to use. After all, can you imagine a world in which you couldn't rustle up a mane of curls in twenty minutes with a set of heated rollers? But do avoid the urge to get hooked on hair gadgets. They must be used with plenty of respect for the hair, plus a certain amount of common sense. Continuous daily use of heated rollers, especially on dry or already porous, processed hair can ruin condition, eliminate shine and drastically alter the colour, because of the shock of such intense heat. Tongs are just as damaging if misused – they should never be so hot that they burn your hand. Provided you resist the temptation to over-use them, styling appliances can nevertheless prove a boon on the odd occasion when you want to jazz up your usual hairstyle and time is of the essence, or in order to experiment with a slightly different look. No matter how pressed you are for time, never use tongs or heated rollers on hair that's damp, and resist the urge to 'overstyle'. Keep contact between hair and appliances to a minimum and condition your hair each time you wash it.

Curling tongs
are ideal for smooth, gentle, wavy styles, or very loose curls. Make sure that you secure the end of each section of hair and then wrap it firmly and smoothly around the tongs avoiding uneven bends and kinks.

Curling brushes
are easier to work with than tongs as the hair cannot escape once you've started the winding process. There is, however, a slight risk of tangling hair if you aren't careful. Brushes are ideal for fixing smaller tighter curls and achieving short styles. Alternatively you can use curling brushes to smooth and straighten longer hair.

Crimpers
are rather like the waffle irons used to make toasted sandwiches. They give a romantic, shimmery, Pre-Raphaelite look to long hair turning it into a mass of tiny symmetrical waves. Fun to use for a special – and occasional – effect, but definitely harmful to hair that's even slightly dry and liable to splitting and breaking.

Dry shampoo
which absorbs excess oils, dirt and lifts flat, lank hair, is another standby. Obviously the effects work better on mousy, blonde or grey hair, while dark hair may look dull and slightly matt.

Hairspray
is still an essential aid for anyone who is not too keen on very tousled, ultra-casual hairstyles, or battling with fine unmanageable hair. Nowadays using hairspray need not transform your head into a lacquer-clogged petrified helmet just in order to keep your style intact. Most modern sprays simply act as an invisible featherlight support, nudging hair into shape and holding it there while allowing it to move and shine naturally. Choose a brand that suits your hair type and make sure you brush out any residue at night.

HAIR PROBLEMS

Human hair – along with skin and nails – is like litmus paper. It keeps constant and accurate tabs on our inner health, reflecting the ups and downs in our general well-being, the food we eat and the drugs we take. Each individual hair, and there are about 100,000 of these on the average adult head, depends for its strength and overall condition on the cell activity and nourishment it receives at root level within the scalp. These tissues are rich in nerve endings and blood vessels which fuel each growing hair with all the nutrition necessary for maintaining shine and strength. Anything therefore that interferes with the flow of blood to the scalp, or alters its quota of nutrients, is eventually bound to alter both the rate and quality of growth. Stress, illness, emotional shock, taking drugs, hormonal changes, crash diets, can all impair circulation and clutter-up the blood supply with poisonous wastes which, just as they make your skin look grey and sallow, affect the basic condition of your hair.

Excessive hair loss
can be triggered by conditions as diverse as anaemia, thyroid problems, coming off the pill, childbirth, taking a long course of antibiotics or prolonged emotional upheaval. If you think you may be losing more than your fair share of hair over a certain period make sure you consult either your doctor or a trichologist to check up on your general health. But don't panic unneccessarily. Most of us lose between fifty and a hundred hairs every day, with slight seasonal fluctuations when this can become either more or less pronounced. It is absolutely no indication that you are heading for baldness – so relax! Hair grows in very definite cycles which include a resting and growing phase, fast summer growth and slower winter growth. Very often nature tends to get out of rhythm and these cycles overlap, causing hair loss to be temporarily more noticeable – rather like a moulting cat or dog! Nervous tension, by making the muscles at the back of the neck and scalp rigid and knotted, can also starve the scalp of its regular blood supply, so try and keep the area relaxed by massaging the scalp gently with the fingertips, moving it in circular motion over the entire head to keep it flexible and the blood vessels unconstricted. Hair is about 95 per cent protein, and as such shows up

unbalanced or outright sloppy eating habits. Fresh fruit, salads, vegetables, fish, dairy produce and wholemeal foods are essential for cultivating lustrous hair. On the other hand, consuming too many sweet foods, salt, smoking and drinking too much alcohol can rapidly lead to excessive oiliness or just boring, lack-lustre hair. If you suspect your diet may be lacking in a lot of basic nutrients try taking a 'tonic' course of wheatgerm and Brewer's yeast – both rich in the B complex vitamins essential for healthy nerve tissue and beautiful strong hair.

Split ends
are nearly always caused by over-zealous brushing (usually with a cheap, nylon brush), tugging your way through knots and tangles, using a cheap alkaline shampoo and a very hot hairdryer or heated rollers, or too much perming or tinting with insufficient conditioning. Like the edges of a frayed robe, these must be trimmed regularly to stop the split from creeping up the hair shaft and making the effect appear worse. Dry and delicate hair is more liable to split, so make sure you treat it carefully; use a good conditioner and invest in a twice-monthly hair pack.

Dandruff
is undoubtedly the commonest scourge to affect both scalp and hair. There are few people who haven't suffered the disorder in one form or another at some point in their lives. Dandruff is often mistakenly classified as a problem that goes hand in hand with overactive sebaceous glands and an oily scalp. Unfortunately it isn't as simple as all that. Exactly what causes dandruff still remains a mystery. Skin is continuously shedding its upper layer in the form of microscopic dead cells, which are normally brushed and washed away so that there's never any build-up or residue. The scalp, however, seems to be particularly sensitive to chemical changes in the body and, as metabolism changes, the surface of the scalp loses large flakes and scaly particles instead of the normal powder-like substance.

Certainly, teenage dandruff is commonly a result of hormonal changes that begin at puberty and make the oil glands work overtime – the cause of acne as well as greasy hair and dandruff. This can carry on into your twenties and is relatively easy to control once you've found a good antiseptic shampoo which successfully controls oiliness, as well as dandruff.

Hair, like skin, reflects poor diet, ill health, lack of sleep and emotional stress, as well as insufficient care.

Severe and persistent dandruff, however, should always be seen by a doctor or trichologist. Often mistaken for true dandruff is a dry flaky scalp which sheds skin particles in the same way as greasy dandruff. Poor circulation may be the culprit in this case (check yourself for muscular tension and stress), or a harsh alkaline hair product, a diet low in fats, protein, vitamins A, D, and B complex or general ill-health. Do not try to treat dandruff with strong antiseptic shampoos – these can create serious scalp irritations. A flaky scalp whether it's dry or oily is invariably extra-sensitive and therefore needs to be treated gently. Use a mild

shampoo formulated for either greasy or dry hair, depending on your hair condition, don't scrub too hard and only use a concentrated dandruff shampoo as a last resort. Avoid over-vigorous shampooing and go easy on brushing if your hair is both greasy and plagued by dandruff. Those hundred strokes a day advocated by grandma are probably the worst punishment you can inflict on problem scalps and hair. Excess greasiness often stems from an inner disorder, eating an unbalanced diet, hormonal problems, stress or worry. Try and correct these as well as using a mild shampoo and an oil-free conditioner.

COLOURING

Although the opportunities to change hair colour have never been greater, safer, or given such authentic effects, it seems many women still have largely unrealistic expectations when it comes to transforming their hair shade. Too much enterprise however, especially if you are using a home product, can often end in disaster.

There are no problems with today's over-the-counter colourants – they are all safe and well-formulated. Mistakes lie in the hands of the user. People shouldn't fight their natural pigmentation, as you can't expect to go ash blonde successfully if you're very dark, say with typical mediterranean colouring. Whatever your colouring, you should only go two or three shades lighter than your natural colour and never attempt to go darker. This is why no reputable hairdresser today likes to bleach hair as it's an extreme process and gives a flat, uniform 'dead' look that's unnatural and looks obviously 'dyed'.

Tinting comprises as much as 50 per cent

of all hair treatments carried out, but today's effects are so subtle and natural that it's virtually impossible to tell if a woman has had her hair tinted – or at any rate that's the ultimate goal of any good colourist! More and more popular are tints that change the tone rather than the shade of the hair. Most effective are the honey gold and hazel blondes, the rich russety red-browns and chestnut shades, and the warm deep sherry and burgundy browns that add sparkle and dimension to brunette hair. Nor need colour changes be drastically irreversible or involve a three-act drama. Nowadays there is a wide range of very different products to choose from, most of which have been perfected to take the terror out of tinting.

Water rinses
are the most superficial and temporary of treatments, designed merely to add colour to the outer cuticle of the hair and wash out with your next shampoo. These can be used to tone in the odd patch of grey or white hair, or to cool brassy blonde tones. Dark shades, however, may come off on clothes and bedlinen.

Semi-permanent tints

only have a toning, not a lightening, effect, although the minute molecules of colour do penetrate the inner cuticle temporarily, gradually fading out after three or four weeks. These are excellent for first-time home tinters and anyone not used to colouring. They add particular richness to brown, red and chestnut tones and liven up dull, mousy brown shades. Semi-permanents are also extremely effective for refreshing the basic colour of hair that's dry and porous, since they enhance the quality and add extra sheen.

Permanent tints

are mixed with hydrogen peroxide which activates their small colour molecules, allowing them to penetrate right into the hair cuticle and there react with the hydrogen peroxide – expanding and becoming locked into the body of the hair. These are the most versatile of all tints, since they can darken or lift natural colour and tone it at the same time. Over-the-counter permanents are effective if you chose a product which will lighten your hair one or two shades – no more.

Highlighting

has become increasingly popular in recent years and it's easy to see why, as it offers the most natural-looking effect that can be achieved with colouring. Highlighting emphasizes the multiplicity and nuances of shade that we all have whatever the basic colour of our hair – often between two and six tones on one head of hair. Any natural hair colour can be improved by using one or more different types of high or low lights, scattering them as densely or as sparsely as you wish. Streaks can be merely tinted – especially on mousy or brown shades – lowlighted with a mild bleach, or highlighted with a stronger bleach. These can also be concentrated on just one section of hair, say the fringe, or just the tips of the hair. The great bonus is that there's no need for the prompt retouching necessary when you use an overall tint, since highlights generally only need 'filling in' after three to four month's regrowth, depending on the style of your hair. The main drawback? Highlighting is a complex, refined and expensive procedure, and can only be carried out by an expert hair colourist at a salon. Never attempt to put highlights in yourself at home, unless you want to end up with hair tones that match the subtlety of a zebra skin!

PERMING

The effects of modern perms are a far cry from the tight, frizzy, straw-like styles of a couple of decades ago. Perming in fact has only recently gained status as a look in itself, incorporating styles that are free, loose, easy to wear, yet bouncing with shine and condition. This is mainly because perming solutions have been greatly improved and modified over the past few years, eliminating the risk element and allowing flyaway, delicate hair to be permed without damage or loss of condition for the first time. Perms aren't necessarily synonymous with obvious curly styles. The concept of perming in the 1980s is to add volume, movement and contour to either smooth or wavy styles, and just lift hair at the roots to stop it lying flat against the head – especially effective on short layered hair. Even tinted or highlighted hair can be permed nowadays provided the condition of your hair leaves nothing to be desired. Of course, if you *do* covet a mass of tight, tiny curls, this effect can still be achieved – but without dryness and frizz, and the danger that your hair may resemble an unruly haystack!

Although home perms are available, it's advisable not to try and save money, but to visit a good hairdresser for an expert perm. He will not only advise you on the correct solution strength for your hair type, but also gauge the exact curler size for the degree of curl you want to achieve. It's important to remember, however, that no matter how successful and gentle the perm you've been given, because the perming process alters the chemical structure of the inner hair shaft in order to reshape it, dryness and a certain porousness may well be a problem unless you condition and retexturize your hair thoroughly. Straightening very curly or frizzy hair – the reverse of perming – is on the other hand a drastic procedure which is damaging to the inner structure of the hair, and no one has yet formulated a cream that doesn't dry the hair out and cause severe breakage. Far better for the curly-haired to make the most of their hair type instead.

SPECIAL TREATMENTS

Hair processing such as tinting or perming and conditioning inevitably go together. A good, in-depth hair treatment not only corrects damaged hair fibres, but ideally should nourish and tone the scalp. Anyone with processed hair should have at least one conditioning treatment a month, maybe more, as whatever you take out of hair must be put back. This can be done with luxurious, creamy hair and scalp packs containing such choice conditioners as avocado wax – rich in water-soluble oils – which are steamed or heated into the hair to provide hair and scalp food. Other treatments include protein creams with added vitamin E, wheatgerm oil, hibiscus

Brunettes develop the greatest sheen and the most natural reddish/chestnut highlights with henna. For fair or mousy hair ring the colour changes with a permanent or semi-permanent tint.

flower, myrtle, olive leaves and lotus blossom – all very gentle, fragrant, natural conditioners. Even today, when artificial colourants are about as refined as they are likely to become, hairdressers often prefer to use natural substances such as camomile and rhubarb root to lighten hair, saffron and marigold for deeper gold blonde tones and sage, cascarilla and walnuts to darken greying hair.

Henna is the best known of all herbal treatments. For centuries vegetable henna has been used to colour and condition the hair of women throughout Africa and Asia and also of westerners, with brunette and black hair, and it is still the finest conditioner available. Part colourant, part conditioner, henna is generally mixed with hot water to a creamy paste and 'seasoned' with black coffee to add depth and richness to the colour, fresh lemon juice to accelerate the red pigment and an egg yolk to keep the mixture moist. Other ingredients that add colour variations to henna are hot red wine (to develop titian tones on mousy hair), vinegar and black tea. Generally, the darker your natural colour the more chestnut will be the final result and the lighter you are the more titian the effect. Brunettes and those with very dark or black hair develop the greatest sheen and mousy shades tend only to develop a nondescript orange/red with minimal lustre. Henna must *never* be used on blonde or fair hair unless you want garish orange-yellow hues. If you are attempting a home application, avoid 'doctored' compound hennas or any colour other than red which is the safest, the best conditioner, and the only authentic variety. The only safe black henna (which is generally only used in salons) is in fact a combination of indigo, a blue pigment, and natural red henna. The two mixed together cancels out the red and produces a dark brown shade known as 'black Persian' henna. Root regrowth needs retouching in the normal way and it's important to avoid colour overlap, since henna stains hair permanently and too many applications can encourage too much redness on the ends of the hair.

Lastly, remember that you will need time for a henna treatment. Mixing is a fine art and can't be rushed; application must be carried out with skill and the pack must be left for about an hour or more. In eastern countries women leave the henna on for up to forty-eight hours, during which time they continually baste it with oil to prevent it from drying out.

MAKE-UP FACTS AND FANTASIES

Subtle understatement: the natural look and sophisticated allure. The shades and formulas of today's cosmetics allow ample scope for subtlety and experiment.

A few decades ago nice girls didn't wear make-up and plain girls just stayed plain. Now, however, the use of make-up is universally accepted and refinements in modern cosmetics have allowed women to master that most elusively challenging of effects – the natural look. As the ultimate art of illusion, successful make-up consists of enhancing features without obvious artifice and de-emphasising flaws and defects – making eyes larger and more radiant, the mouth fuller and softer –

without ever seeming over-made-up. Mastering the natural look, explains renowned visagiste Olivier Euchaudemaison, artistic director of one of France's leading cosmetic companies, means studying your skin tone, face shape and individual features in minute detail in order to determine which skin products will best embellish your looks without overwhelming or distorting them. Successful make-up, he believes, is perfecting the art of the possible.

FOUNDATION
your second skin

You must never try to change your skin tone completely. The main aim of effective foundation is to enhance it and camouflage its less attractive characteristics. Remember, when choosing foundation it's best to test a little on the inside of your wrist where the skin comes as close as possible to that of your complexion. Ideally, however, you should rub a little into your jawline and look at it in daylight to find a shade which matches your skin. Although skin tones vary tremendously, they can be broken up into certain principal groups:

Ivory
– very pale, translucent skin that generally accompanies black, dark brown, or auburn hair. Choose a matching foundation.

Cream
– a light, slightly peachy beige that is the typical 'English Rose' complexion which needs a foundation that's either a fraction lighter or darker.

Fair
– a delicate blush-like tone that tends to go with blonde hair. Try and match it exactly.

Pink
– a rosy complexion which can become ruddy, often accompanying red hair and freckles. A beige will tone it down subtly.

Olive
– usually teams with brown eyes and brown or blonde hair. It can look sallow in the winter. Pick an olive foundation or a warm biscuity beige for a healthier look.

Brown
– this may vary from a suntanned complexion, to light coffee or very dark brown. Darker tones often don't need foundation, otherwise try and match it exactly, avoiding tan or bronze shades with a pink or brick-orange pigment.

Feel and texture

The type of foundation you choose depends to a large extent on your skin type, the 'feel' of foundation on your skin, as well as the effect you want to achieve. The choice is enormous today. There are

Smooth on tinted foundation with a damp latex make-up sponge.

Minimize dark circles beneath the eyes with tiny dots of concealing cream, blended **well into the skin where the shadow falls.**

Press loose powder firmly onto the skin, skimming off any surplus.

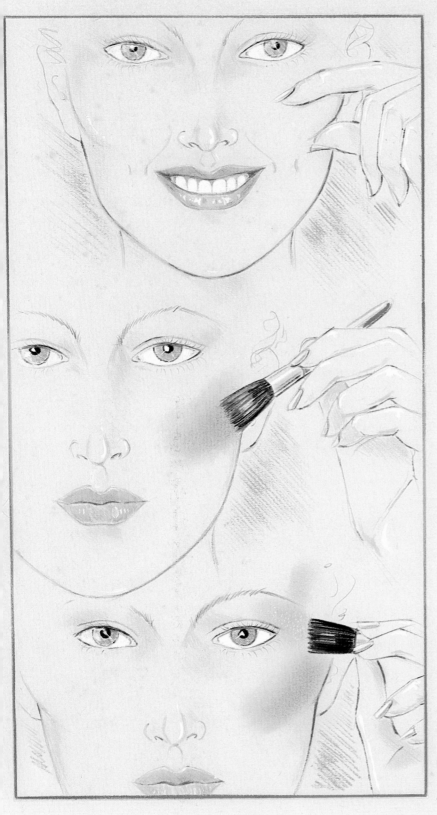

ultra lightweight tinted moisturizers which add a mere trace of colour to the face and are perfect for young, unblemished skins and a very unmade-up look. Fine fluid foundations that give a lightweight but even coverage to the complexion are probably most suitable, while thicker cream foundations give a more opaque coverage hiding tiny flaws and problems such as broken veins and scars. Heavy pan-stick foundations and all-in-one cream powders have long passed out of fashion but they are still available and you may find them useful for camouflaging deeper scars, birthmarks and other blemishes.

An invaluable standby in your make-up kit is concealer stick or cream – a matt buff-coloured product which will erase and soften dark circles underneath the eyes. Use very sparingly and blend in well after applying foundation.

Apply liquid foundation with a latex make-up sponge for a smooth, even finish. Cream foundation or pan-stick needs blending in with the fingertips. Having achieved a perfect and even colour tone don't ruin it by topping up with tinted face powder. These are gradually becoming a relic of the past since the suspension and distribution of pigment in creams and liquids has been so refined and perfected as to appear totally natural. Colourless, translucent powder should be pressed into the skin with cotton wool or a flat powder puff to 'set' the tone you've achieved, creating a matt yet radiant effect without any trace of colour 'build-up'. Use loose powder when you first apply your make-up and pressed powder for repair jobs and renewing make-up during the day.

CONTOURING
light and shade

The use of blusher can be as simple or as complex as you wish. For a healthy, natural outdoor look simply flick a trace of powder blusher, gel or cream rouge onto the fullest part of your cheek. Pinky brown, damson or tawny peach are the most flattering shades, but take care they don't clash with the clothes you're wearing. Cream or gel rouge goes on *over* your foundation but *underneath* your powder, powder blusher glides on *over* your powder. Hollowing or sculpting a round face or very full cheeks can be achieved with a sludgy-brown, matt powder.

To apply blusher correctly, press the thumb and forefinger against the bony structure of the cheek which lies at an angle between the middle of the ear and the base of the nose.

Apply colour along this line and also dust beneath it.

To accentuate the bone structure further, lightly trace a paler, frosted blusher or highlighter along

the upper crest of the cheek near the eyes and around the temples, up to the hairline.

EYES
your most stunning feature

Before making up your eyes, study them carefully in the mirror – their shape and size, whether prominent, deepset or droopy, and the overall impact they create facially. Large, dark, well-shaped eyes with dark lashes are a natural attribute that need relatively little contouring or definition to bring them into focus; small, deepset eyes, however, need extra embellishment.

As far as eye-shadows go, browns and greys are the perennial classic shades that every woman can wear successfully, but be more selective when choosing brighter colours. Blue, turquoise or purple look stunning on blue, grey or greeny grey eyes; marine colours – olive green or moss – intensify hazel eyes; warm cinnamons, beiges, pink or mauve-tinged shades add

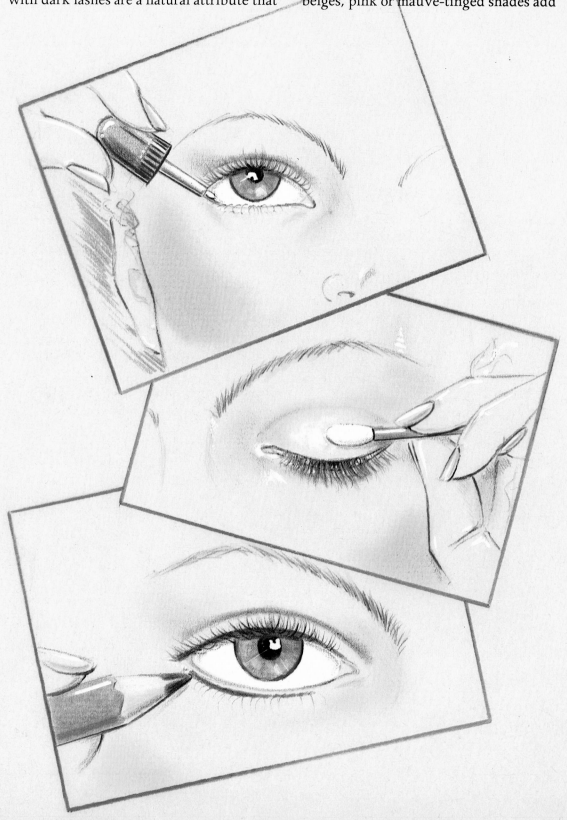

DAYTIME EYES
Refresh sore, gritty or red eyes with eyedrops.

Apply a muted browny-beige, soft grey or sage green powder shadow over the entire eye-lid with a sponge applicator, dove-tailing the colour out and up towards the browbone.

Trace a very fine crayon line along the base of the top and bottom lashes to emphasize the shape of the lids and focus the colour and sparkle of the eyes.

50

warmth and sparkle to brown eyes. Powder shadow is hard to beat for easy application and staying power. Cream shadow goes on like silk but tends to crease and shine after a few hours. To avoid 'sweaty' lids powder well before and after.

The mascara you use depends largely on the sensitivity of your eyes, the length and thickness of your lashes and the effect you want to create. Waterproof mascara prevents smudging and running and is great if you lead a hectic, busy, outdoor or sporty life, while it also makes lashes longer and thicker. Special 'building' mascaras with added ingredients to coat and lengthen the lashes can irritate the eyes and prove hard to remove, though the effect they give is pure Hollywood glamour! There are special conditioning mascaras to stop the lashes turning brittle and to encourage growth, and if you have particularly sensitive eyes – and skin – or wear contact lenses, look out for hypo-allergenic eye make-up. Always apply two coats of mascara, allowing each application to dry thoroughly.

For extra definition, apply a dark, frosted shadow over the eyelid, smoothing a darker shade into the natural creaseline, to add depth to the eye colour.

Two coats of waterproof mascara on the top and bottom lashes 'open' the eye and give a soft starry effect. To build up thickness and length without smudging, allow each application to dry thoroughly.

Tidy eyebrows by brushing them upwards into a gentle arch with a baby's toothbrush or a dampened mascara brush. Add a touch of vaseline to control thicker eyebrows and add shine.

51

EVENING GLAMOUR

Define the eyelid by tracing a very fine pencil line or a thread of liquid or cake liner along the upper lashes, extending this very slightly at the outside corner.

Blend a mid-tone, vibrant shadow over the entire lid, using a damp drush for extra depth of tone.

Accentuate deep hollows with a darker, smokier shadow in the creaseline, gently blending and fading out the colour towards the browbone.

Very pale frosted shadow or highlighter on the crest of the browbone projects bone structure, adding sheen and sparkle to both skin and eyes.

Single, false eyelashes build a thick, romantic fringe around the entire eye without hardness or giveaway baselines. Grip each lash with tweezers, dip base into a drop of surgical glue, press firmly against your own top or bottom eyelashes. An excellent trick for 'filling in' gaps in sparse lashes.

LIPS
soft and luscious

You can improve significantly on thin, flat or small lips, building up the shape and roundness of your mouth with lip crayon, using a pale brown or a colour that's one shade darker than your lipstick. Alternatively outline the lips with a firm, pointed lipbrush. Full lips can get away with just about any shade of lipstick no matter how bright or bold. A smaller mouth, however, looks softer with the subtle pinks, beiges, peaches and browns as well as frosted shades. Wearing a slightly paler shade on the inside of the lips makes a small mouth appear fuller. If you prefer a natural look use a transparent colourless lip gloss, a lip tint that gives a bare hint of colour or lip salve to stop your lips from drying out.

To prevent the new softer texture lipsticks and pencils from 'creeping' into the fine lines around the mouth, extend your foundation and powder right down to the lips and then trace a good outline with a crayon or lip brush over the powder.

PARTY LOOKS

The essential rule to remember for evening make-up is that strong lights sap your complexion of its colour – so with all your cosmetics choose a slightly warmer shade than you normally wear during the day. Blusher comes into its own in the evening – experiment with stronger pinks and peaches and build up the colour more intensely. Little pots of multicoloured irridescent powder which you can buy will create a rich and diverse juxtaposition of colours on the eyes. Lips can get away with

For a perfectly shaped, neat lip line first trace the outer contours with either a browny-beige lip crayon or a lip brush dipped in your usual lipstick. Do not exaggerate the lipline or go too far outside your natural shape. Next fill in main colour with a flattish lipbrush. Finally, blot well with tissue to 'set' the colour and shape.

deeper or brighter, more electric lipstick
tones in the evenings; shades that might
look hard or garish in daylight come into
their own after dark, when the soft colours
you normally wear appear washed out.

TOOLS OF THE TRADE

Once you've found the products that suit
you, expert application becomes the key to
successful make-up. It's impossible to
achieve a natural looking, long-lasting and
truly professional finish without using the
correct 'tools'. It's worth investing a little
extra money in these since good quality
brushes will last far longer than the
cheaper variety while allowing you to
carry out all the tiny subtleties needed to
master a particular look.

Brushes
The most important item in any make-up
kit. You'll need a full, soft, slightly flattish
brush to apply blusher and a second one
for your highlighter in order to avoid
colour or glitter 'spillover', as well as a
very fine, pointed lip liner and a flat
wedge-shaped brush made of slightly
tougher bristles that don't separate for
applying eyeshadow (again invest in two
or three to use with different colours).
Wedge-shaped sponge applicators which
are excellent for blending powder shadow
more easily – especially if you are mixing
them with water. Also invaluable are a
small toothbrush for tidying the eyebrows,
and a flat, broad, pointed lipbrush to both
outline and fill in the lips. You may also
need a large, soft chubby brush to flick off
surplus powder and skim away flecks of
eyeshadow that stray onto the face. If you
like using block mascara choose the
thickest mascara brush you can find for
rapid and effective coverage.

Pencil sharpener
You'll need to use this regularly to keep
kohl pencils, eye and lip crayons pointed.

Sponges
A fine latex 'wedge' sponge is ideal for
applying liquid foundation with a light
touch so that you don't get a heavy or
uneven streaky effect. Keep it clean by
rinsing out after each application.

Cotton buds
Invaluable for mopping up smudged eyeliner or mascara especially beneath the
lashes and for tidying up eye make-up.

EATING FOR BEAUTY AND GOOD HEALTH

You've heard it said time and time again: we are what we eat. A healthy diet is the cornerstone to longlasting good health, and will inevitably be reflected in our skin, eyes, figure and hair, as well as in our energy levels and resistance to illness. A healthy diet, however, does not depend on rigorously avoiding certain foods while concentrating on other 'permitted' ones, but on a balanced and varied diet that includes enough but not too much of all the different types of food.

Unfortunately, the hectic pace of modern life means that it is all too easy to adopt erratic, unbalanced and therefore unhealthy eating patterns. This might mean simply taking in more food energy than the body can use, which means that all those unused calories eventually turn to fat and we become overweight, or eating too much of one type of food to the exclusion of other important items.

Irregular meals are equally unhealthy. Many of us are guilty of perhaps missing breakfast, possibly just existing on cups of tea or coffee and the odd biscuit during the morning and lunch hour, eating a sticky bun or chocolate bar in the afternoon, and then gorging on a heavy three-course meal in the evening. Skipping meals in this way merely means that you're a likely candidate for a range of symptoms including low blood sugar, tiredness, lethargy, irritability, poor concentration, headaches and indigestion.

GETTING THE BALANCE RIGHT

As a guide to striking the right balance in your diet, look at the main food categories listed here. You should try to eat something from groups A to E each day, checking that you get plenty of variety within each group and don't always eat the same things. Watch your intake of E, F and G, especially if you are trying to lose weight.

A Cereals: bread and other flour products, pasta, rice, breakfast cereals
B Meat, fish, offal, poultry, eggs, cheese and milk
C Vegetables: root, leafy, legumes
D Fruits: citrus and other
E Fats and oils, including butter, margarine, cooking and salad oil
F Confectionery and sweets
G Alcohol

In this way you should obtain all the essential vitamins, minerals, trace elements, protein and dietary fibre needed for peak health. It's important to remember that *no one food* contains all the nutrients needed for good physical and mental health, so try to eat as wide a range of foods as possible. Remember too that your energy demands vary according to age and occupation. They are likely to be higher if you are physically active, during pregnancy or while you are breastfeeding.

FAST AND CONVENIENCE FOODS

When we are very busy, working long or erratic hours, trying to stick to a tight budget or just plain lazy, it's particularly tempting to overlook many of the basic rules of healthy eating and resort to easy-to-prepare, quick-to-eat convenience foods. While there is nothing harmful or unduly unhealthy in eating this type of food occasionally, keep a check on how they are incorporated into your diet, and never rely on them to the exclusion of a balanced and varied diet. Relying on any one food, whether convenience or fresh is likely to run the risk of some sort of dietary deficiency.

Keep a check also on the amount of 'snack' foods you eat. Single items such as an apple, a chocolate bar, crisps or a bowl of soup, are not really adequate substitutes for a meal, although they can play an important part in the overall diet. In the end, however, the best rule is to use your own discretion; after all, being faddy about your diet can be as harmful as neglecting it all together.

COOKING METHODS

The way that you prepare and cook food also has a tremendous bearing on its nutritional value, and can help make meals interesting and varied. Choose the best quality and the freshest products you can afford. Try to eat as many vegetables as you can raw, and when you do cook them make sure you don't destroy minerals and vitamins by using too much liquid or overcooking them. For maximum nutritional goodness – and taste – try and steam vegetables whenever possible. Salads should be eaten the moment you've prepared them, since cutting and shredding releases a lot of the vitamins and minerals in the vegetables. Don't buy food in too large quantities because fresh produce deteriorates quickly and try to check that vegetables and fruit haven't been lying around in the shop for long periods of time.

Use salt in moderation, most people need substantially less than they consume. Make sure also that you don't buy fatty cuts of meat; not only can too much fat be harmful, but if you are going to trim it off anyway you are not getting the amount of meat you've paid for. The most expensive cuts of meat, however, are certainly no more nutritious than cheaper ones and it's worth bearing in mind that using fresh herbs can add flavour and interest to many a dish, while providing additional vitamins into the bargain.

WHEN TO EAT

Timing is an important element of healthy eating. Try to begin the day for instance by eating a reasonably satisfying breakfast. Fruit juice, yoghourt, an egg, cereal, wholemeal toast with butter and marmalade and tea and coffee for example, will help to raise your energy levels and keep them steady for the first half of the day by maintaining adequate supplies of blood sugar to keep your brain alert and clear. Avoid the temptation to skip lunch – when most of us feel in need of a boost to keep us going. Generally speaking a light lunch, either hot or cold, is preferable to a rich heavy one which can leave you feeling lethargic and bloated. Make sure that you don't eat your last meal too late at night, especially if it's the main meal of the day. Eating a lot of rich food late in the evening can lead to indigestion, heartburn and sleeplessness.

Provided you stick to eating three satisfying meals a day you should be able to resist the temptation to nibble extra snacks that you don't need. Many people, however, prefer to eat smaller meals more frequently throughout the day; don't worry about this, but do check that you are keeping to a good nutritional mix in your food.

VEGETARIAN EATING

If you don't enjoy eating meat or fish, or simply feel healthier by cutting these out of your diet altogether, you can do this quite safely without harming your health. Make up for any protein deficit by eating more beans and pulses, and take care to include in your diet plenty of green vegetables, wholemeal bread and wholegrain cereals to avoid low levels of iron and vitamin B12.

If you follow a vegan diet which cuts out meat, fish, fowl and all dairy produce, it is wise to consult your doctor or contact The Vegan Society in order to find out the best ways of ensuring that you enjoy an adequate diet throughout the year. A vegetarian or vegan diet will entail cutting out several main food groups from your diet, although one based around lentils, soya beans and other legumes, dried fruit, nuts, wheatgerm, wholegrain products, yeast and molasses can certainly meet your body's nutritional requirements. Take care, however, to keep your diet varied. The Vegetarian Society will also be able to give you information about this.

SLIMMING DIETS

Whatever you may have read to the contrary in diet books and magazines, there is unfortunately no fast or easy way to lose a lot of surplus weight or achieve a slimmer, trimmer figure. The reason why most people have a weight problem in the first place (unless of course they have a glandular orametabolic disorder) is quite simply because they take in more food than they burn up – whether in the form of protein, carbohydrate or fat – allowing the body to convert this extra energy into fat. This may be due to compulsive 'fingering' as a result of boredom, depression or unhappiness, taking insufficient exercise, or eating too many energy-rich foods, especially fat and sugar.

You can only become slimmer and stay that way by mastering enough patience and willpower to overcome bad dietary habits and generally re-educating your eating patterns for life. While this inevitably means cutting the urge to overeat and trying not to gorge yourself, it also involves sticking to a balanced and varied diet while cutting calories. Take a look at your regular eating patterns and try to work out exactly which ones are causing your body to build up stores of too much excess fuel in the form of fat. For some people, losing that distressing surplus stone may be simply a matter of cutting out sugar in tea and coffee, spreading less butter on bread, omitting jam and honey from the breakfast table, eating potatoes baked or boiled in their skins rather than fried, steaming vegetables and grilling meat and eating them 'unadorned' rather than swimming in rich, thick sauces. The less fattening cooking methods such as steaming, grilling and baking can also help to make you not only more adventurous in how you prepare and serve food, but, best of all, they can teach you to appreciate its natural flavour. For added subtlety and piquancy, try using herbs or lemon juice to flavour meat, fish, poultry, vegetables, legumes, salads and rice.

Starving yourself or following un-balanced crash diets for long periods can be extremely damaging to your health, however severe your weight problem. Most fashionable slimming diets are based on cutting out or down on certain major food categories and consequently they are neither satisfying, interesting nor well-balanced enough to stick to for very long. Although crash diets can often help you to lose quite a lot of weight over a period of a couple of weeks, inevitably you will regain the weight once you resume your normal eating habits.

BODY CARE – GETTING TO GRIPS WITH STRESS

Although you may not always be aware of it at the time, modern stress and the tensions of twentieth-century life are probably the greatest enemy of your looks, not to mention your general well-being. Stress of course is nothing new, for hundreds of years man has lived and coped with wars, plagues, fires, famine, poverty and a host of other factors that created upheaval and unrest in his life. But it has now been medically proven that it's not so much the major upheavals that are harmful to us, but the nagging day-to-day irritants that build up, often unnoticed, eventually causing chronic worry, anxiety, depression, anger and, most damaging of all, nervous tension, which have no opportunity for outlet and release. The final result is that this tension gets 'stored' in the body, particularly in the nervous system, leading to such familiar stress symptoms as insomnia, migraine, backache, indigestion and many other chronic ailments. The chemical cause of stress isn't hard to understand. When we are suddenly faced with a stressful situation – say an exam, an interview for a job, a family quarrel, a bad traffic jam – the body automatically puts itself on to 'full alert' releasing large quantities of extra stress hormones such as adrenalin and noradrenalin into the bloodstream to provide extra energy, increasing the heart-beat and breath rate, raising the blood pressure and the pulse rate, speeding up the digestive system, and increasing the flow of blood to the muscles to increase their power. This is what scientists call man's primitive 'fight or flight' response that for thousands of years has ensured his survival and evolution by preparing him against attack. Our ancestors, however, never wasted their survival 'kit', when the moment of danger had passed or the kill had been completed this emergency response immediately switched itself off and the body returned to a normal and relaxed state. The problem today, however, with modern pressures and stresses is that they very often don't resolve themselves; bad traffic is commonplace, pressures at work or at home often build up rather than blow over, with the result that our body frequently switches over to a tense state – and very often stays that way until physical and mental exhaustion causes us to break down and become ill.

'No one nowadays is immune to the ill effects of stress', emphasized David Lieber, managing director of a leading slimming and beauty centre. 'Even very young people can suffer from the pace and pressures put upon them by modern life. Also , the fact that people are less inclined to take exercise, eat too many of the wrong foods, have bad posture, and swallow medicines to deal with all sorts of aches and pains means that they are usually very

are a number of different systems which you can use to help you become more relaxed and more able to cope with stress: yoga, meditation, bio-feedback, self-hypnosis are all tried, tested and highly successful methods, but most require a definite period of study and the help of a teacher. Doing simple relaxation exercises to turn off physically and mentally at home can prove just as effective, providing you do them regularly, preferably at the same time every day.

COUNTDOWN TO PERFECT RELAXATION

Put aside fifteen to twenty minutes and avoid any disturbances such as phone calls and knocks on the door. Choose a well-ventilated, quiet, slightly darkened room with enough space for you to lie flat on the floor. Put on some quiet background music – something slow and rythmical – loosen all tight and restrictive clothing and take off any jewellery. Now prepare to switch off: this should be the one and only goal in your life at this particular moment.

1 Lie with your palms upward, knees loose, feet relaxed and slightly splayed apart.

2 Become aware of your breathing. Are you taking short shallow breaths, using only the top of your chest? This is one of the most common signs of tension. To correct your breathing, imagine as you inhale that your abdomen is a large vacuum; you're taking air into this space, blowing it out like a balloon. Then, as you exhale, feel the air travelling back through your chest and let it out through the throat, hearing yourself breathe out. At the same time lower the jaw and let the tongue rest on the lower teeth. Repeat this gently for a few minutes savouring the rhythm and sensation of your breathing.

3 Begin to think of relaxing each part of your body in turn: feet, calves, knees, thighs, stomach, back, chest, shoulders, neck, arms, hands and face. Imagine that tension is coiled up in each of these parts of the body like a spring. Try to make each coil gradually unwind, until all the tension has disappeared, saying to yourself 'tense . . . relax' as you feel the muscles relaxing and becoming limp. Try to relax the lower part of your spine, so that it lies flat against the floor.

Stress, tension and aggression – inevitable results of our lifestyle today. Relaxation can help to combat stress and safeguard looks and health.

ill-equipped to control the amount of stress in their lives.'

However, although we may have largely lost the art of relaxing naturally, practising 'stress control' is relatively easy once you've found a method that suits you and you make it an integral routine of your daily life. It's no use practising relaxation or breathing exercises every now and again and expecting to feel cool and calm. Just like exercising to keep fit, relaxing should become a way of life and a ritual that you look forward to. What's more there's little mystique attached to relaxation. All you need is a quiet room, total privacy for twenty minutes and a good imagination! Instead of seeking relaxation from outside sources, like watching TV, drinking and smoking, it should come from within as a form of self awareness and control. There

4 Now that you've isolated and driven tension out of every part of the body (check that there isn't still some stubborn muscle harbouring stiffness and stress) it's time to move into isolating and relaxing the mind. Concentrate on one particular and beautiful, restful image – a lake, stream, mountains, the ocean – and at the same time visualize one predominant colour. 'Hold' the image in your mind, creating an inner space that's filled entirely with your basic image and the colour that you've chosen. At this stage you are at a fairly advanced level of relaxation, when the pulse rate begins to drop and your body is at the same stage of rest as during deep sleep. Once you can reach this state fairly easily and regularly, then you'll find that you can control your body and its response to stress far more effectively. Mastering body control of this sort even means difficult goals such as dieting and giving up smoking become far easier to achieve.

Relaxation exercises are first and foremost designed to strengthen your 'stress defences', and wind down the body if it's tense and tired. They are also an ideal way of overcoming sleeplessness and headaches, two common and disturbing by-products of a stressful life which almost all of us have suffered at some time.

We all take sleep very much for granted – that is until our sleep patterns start to go awry, leading to two a.m. waking and disrupted, fitful sleep that makes you feel more tired than refreshed, or simply the inability to drop off! Insomnia in itself is of course pretty harmless. No one ever became ill or died through lack of sleep since the body *does* eventually go to sleep when it is tired enough. Also, it's a common misconception that we all need the same amount of sleep. Eight hours sleep is by no means a norm that applies to every one of us. How many hours you find you need to sleep depends entirely on your metabolism, your age, your body type, the amount of mental and physical energy you expend, and your lifestyle generally. Sleeplessness, however, is a very clear warning that you are either:

A too tense and worried about the day's activities to be able to unwind sufficiently.

B suffering from a minor complaint like indigestion which means that a part of your body is working and not at rest.

C there is something worrying you subconsciously and your sleep is disturbed in an attempt to resolve the problem.

D your environment is unsuited to restful sleep – an uncomfortable bed, too much or too little fresh air, too much noise or light.

Learning to relax should help tremendously in clearing your mind, unwinding the body and so preparing you for a good night's sleep. Don't embark on the exercises immediately before going to bed, six or eight p.m. is about the latest time you should do them. Taking exercise helps to make you healthily tired and works off any stored tension – but again not just before bedtime. Having a warm bath, reading a boring book, listening to some soft gentle music, can help make you feel more sleepy and drop off more easily. Try not to eat a big meal late in the evening, since it's heavy going on your stomach and digestive system. Hot milky drinks, however, can often make you relaxed and sleepy, as milk contains an amino acid that helps the brain produce certain important 'sleep' chemicals. Camomile is a soothing herbal alternative, while peppermint tea helps settle the digestion before going to bed. The most damaging thing you can do to your health is of course to take sleeping pills or tranquillizers. Not only can they become addictive, but they are *not* a solution to the problem, as they mask the true causes of insomnia and produce an artificial form of sleep which can often leave you feeling drugged and woozy the next morning. Above all, too much worry about not sleeping can encourage those wakeful nights. Changes in the weather, pre-menstrual tension and changes in diet can all effect the way you sleep, and the less you worry about sleeplessness the sooner the problem will pass.

Headaches and migraines are a much more unpleasant offshoot of nervous tension and generally are harder to treat. A twenty minute relaxation period can positively help in easing muscular tightness and so help to shift headaches. Simple neck and head rolling exercises can loosen tight muscles at the back of the neck and the tops of the shoulders, which generally trigger headaches. Migraines, however, may be directly linked to certain foods you eat – in particular chocolate, cheese, orange juice, wine, dairy produce – so you may need to do some detective work on your normal diet. Headaches and migraine can also be a problem just before and during your period, so make sure you relax and get plenty of rest at this time. If you *do* suffer from persistent and troublesome headaches consult your doctor about the problem.

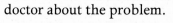

stomach pulled in, back straight but not rigid because all backs have a natural curve, shoulders, neck and arms relaxed. By all means shift your weight from one foot to the other, but don't push your hip joints or buttocks out of alignment as this is not only ugly, but can lead to lower backache and poor circulation.

How do you rate your walking style? Do you walk slowly, dragging your feet, shoulders slumped and back slouching forwards, eyes downcast, so that they never take in the sky, trees, tops of buildings, or other people? Bad posture becomes glaringly obvious when we're in motion, because it distorts the smoothness, rhythm and alignment of the body. We often carry things in a clumsy way, allowing heavy shopping bags to dislocate shoulders and arms, or outsize handbags to tip-tilt the upper half of the body and create backstrain. The longer you are unaware of such bad habits the more restricting they become, putting a brace on the body and making it rigid when it should be free. The first part of you that suffers if you have bad posture is your back. After all back pain accounts for more sickness and absenteeism in this country than any other complaint, a problem which could be often avoided if we paid more attention to correcting our posture.

Exercise techniques based on physical realignment such as the famous 'Alexander Technique' rely entirely on restoring health by teaching you to move and stand without putting strain on the body. Poor posture also saps the body of energy; walk with your head high, back upright, with a spring in your step, legs swinging out from the hips and you are less likely to get bogged down with aching feet and general fatigue at the end of the day. These's even a correct and incorrect way to sleep. While a soft mattress makes the body compensate for its lack of overall support by shifting and contorting into different positions, a hard mattress literally throws you into the correct position, cutting down on disturbed sleep, cramps and backache. Remember also not to strain your back when pushing heavy objects or bending down to pick up anything from the floor; try to use your stomach muscles not your back to take the strain out of extra physical exertion. When bending down to pick up a heavy suitcase or a bag of vegetables, keep your body upright, stomach in, and bend at the knees only taking the full weight of the object you're lifting up with you as you swing back into a standing position.

Correct posture, whether at work or play, not only reduces physical tension but also allows you to breathe properly and helps to prevent backache and other chronic aches and pains. Furthermore, it improves body contours and encourages gracefulness.

POSTURE
uses and abuses

Sloppy, incorrect posture is also guaranteed to load your body with extra tension. For instance, most of us are guilty of sitting slumped or curled up like a sack of potatoes on a chair at some time or other during the day. Our breathing becomes shallow, the lungs are unable to expand, the neck and shoulders get tense and the chest area is constricted. Extra strain builds up if you spend a lot of time typing or writing in a distorted position and the same goes for standing over long periods. Waiting for trains and buses in the freezing cold, or queueing in shops and stations is inevitably tedious and a bit of a strain on the legs, but you'll take a lot of the slog out of standing if you correct your posture – weight evenly distributed on both feet,

MASSAGE
the oldest therapy in the world

The origins of massage date back thousands of years. The use of scented oils to heal, relax and calm the body dates as far back as the civilizations of ancient Greece and Egypt, and today different forms of massage have become popular in the treatment of everything from hair loss and skin problems to anxiety and tension. Nor does massage necessarily involve spending lots of time and money on professional treatments. Everybody can learn the basics of different massage techniques, after all, in China, Japan and India massage has been recognized as a home therapy for centuries, that members of a family practice on one another to stay fit and healthy, as well as to treat minor aches, pains, and illnesses. Anyone, even a child, can master the principle of massage and use it amongst family and friends.

The very simplest massage method comes from China and is based on the guiding rules of acupuncture, except that you use finger pressure instead of needles. Acupressure (or *shiatsu* as it is called in Japan) works by stimulating the body's various reflex points – there are over 800 dotted all over the body – and so improving the flow of energy and circulation in specific parts of the body, as well as eliminating muscular tension. The feet have a particularly dense collection of reflex points which connect to every area in the rest of the body and therefore the soles, sides, toes and tops of the feet should always get a lot of attention in any acupressure massage. By looking at a person's expression while you're massaging their feet, you can tell a lot about what is wrong with them, as each point on the foot corresponds to an organ or area of the body. The face too is covered in different points which you can treat more specifically to banish colds, headaches, sore eyes and tiredness. The hands contain many important key reflex zones such as the *hoku* point that controls pain relief. Dentists and doctors who use acupuncture instead of conventional anaesthetics always stimulate this point to prevent a patient feeling discomfort and pressing this area often gives fast and total relief for migraines.

General massage

The object of any massage is to make you feel more relaxed. It is easy for a masseuse to locate a person's main tension spots, by laying her hands flat over areas like the shoulders, nape of the neck, small or top of the back, tension in the muscles can be felt like tight cords. Relaxed muscles are rather like putty; firm and flexible, never rock hard. You can ease tension by gently kneading these muscles and rubbing them with a firm, circular motion, pressing into the flesh without pinching or hurting. Always use a fragrant oil to help make the skin soft and supple, as well as create a luxurious atmosphere!

If you are going to give a more thorough overall massage, make sure your partner is lying face down on a firm, flat surface (the floor will do), hands relaxed on either side of the body, head to one side. Begin by putting your hands on the lower back, exerting a comfortable amount of pressure, then keep pushing as you slowly follow the muscles upwards along the sides of the spine. Open the hands up over the top of the back then pull them along the sides of the body down to the waist. Start the massage like this to encourage relaxation before you begin working at specific knotted areas, finishing afterwards with the same broad sweeping movements. Massage can relieve a lot of stiffness and soreness after an all-out bout of sports or jogging, or even dancing. Whenever the muscles have been contracting for a period of time, you should stretch and massage them to help counteract muscle spasm and the risk of cramp. Patting and pinching the calves and rubbing the thighs, knees and ankles, prevents muscle fatigue and also means you won't build up ugly bunched muscles.

Recontouring massage

Because of the toning effects on the skin and muscle tissue and the stimulus of blood and lymph circulation, massage has long been recognized as the ideal therapy for figure problems such as slack and flabby muscles, rough unconditioned skin, stubborn patches of localized fat and also stretch marks. Of course there's no need to invest a lot of money in a massage course – unless you want to indulge in some unashamed pampering. One of the benefits of localized massage is that you can do a lot of it on yourself – once you've learned a few simple guidelines. The best time to massage is immediately after you've had your bath or shower, when the skin is still moist and

Massage induces physical as well as mental and emotional well-being. It can tone, recontour and condition the body tissues as well as improve circulation.

warm. There are special ivy-or seaweed-
based creams on the market, which have
been especially designed to stimulate the
circulation and help break down fatty
tissue, provided you massage them in
regularly and correctly.

The most obvious parts of the body that
respond to massage are the thighs, knees,

hips, waist – all areas that you can easily get to grips with. Regular massage is the only way to tackle the problem of cellulite – those lumps and bulges at the top of the outer thigh – which may not respond to exercise or dieting. You can tell when you've got cellulite: the skin looks pitted and gives a dimpled 'orange peel' effect when you pinch it, showing lots of tiny hard nodules of fat just beneath the skin's surface. Firm circular movements with the palm of the hand encourages the circulation and the elimination of waste products in the system, while kneeding, wringing, knuckling, and very gentle pinching movements help to soften and disperse the fatty lumps. Never manipulate the areas so agressively that you bruise the skin or make the flesh red and painful. If you are trying to whittle down your thighs, or any other lumpy, bumpy areas you should give yourself at least five to ten minutes' massage a day. Of course massage alone won't do the trick; keep a check on your diet, avoid salt and spicy food, drink plenty of water – six to eight glasses per day – and cut down on coffee, tea and alcohol. Bathtime can also double up as an opportunity to massage. Use a rough hemp mitt or a friction glove to whip up the circulation on buttocks, thighs, hips, stomach and keep the skin silky and smooth. This will also help to open the pores and soften the skin in preparation for your main massage after your bath.

Acupressure points

Press each point for a count of thirty seconds with your middle finger or thumb.

1 To relieve headaches, press both of your temples about an inch from the edge of the eyebrows.
2 To clear stuffy nose and blocked sinuses, press the points running along the sides of the nose, starting at the nostrils and working up to the corner of the eyes. Lastly press the 'third eye' point right between the eyebrows.
3 To refresh tired eyes, press the front, centre and outer edge of each eyebrow. Then repeat on matching points underneath the bottom eyelids.
4 To relieve toothache or neuralgia, press the point right in front of your ear at the bottom edge of the cheek bone.
5 To reduce a craving for food or general faintness, press the centre of your upper lip about a quarter of an inch below the nose.
6 To control migraines and tension headaches, press the *hoku* point on the top of the hand. To locate it, crook your left thumb and place your other thumb at a slight angle onto the fleshy part between the thumb and index finger and squeeze hard.

Acupressure points
Below. To relieve headaches (1). Below right. To clear blocked sinuses (2).

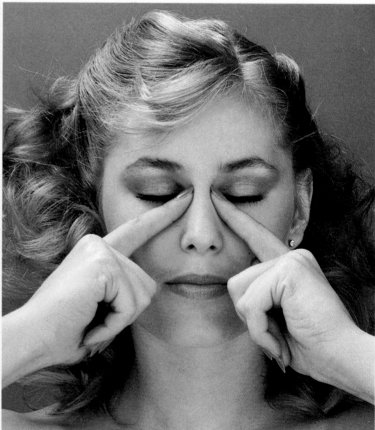

Feet

There are literally dozens of reflex points all over the soles, sides, backs of the feet and on the base of each toe. Simply covering the entire area of both feet with lots of firm pressing movements with the edge of the thumb helps to relax and invigorate you when you're tired and tense, while also providing a delicious foot treatment. If any part of the foot feels sore or particularly rigid keep pressing and making tiny semicircular movements with your thumb to get the circulation going and to disperse any built-up waste matter that has accumulated.

YOGA
the simplest route to fitness and harmony

Many people make the mistake of thinking that yoga is only for the very fit. Unfortunately all those pictures of lithe double-jointed girls in advanced yoga positions suggest you have to be a contortionist to take it up in the first place, but nothing could be further from the truth. Yoga is the oldest form of keep fit in the world and its present day appeal is certainly due to the fact that *anyone* can take it up at any time in their lives and experience tremendous health benefits. Yoga is unique in that it not only exercises and strengthens all parts of the body, including the internal glands and organs, helping them to function more smoothly, but at the same time it encourages deep mental relaxation and improved circulation, through emphasis on special breathing techniques. Yoga literally translated means union, therefore the entire body gets stronger through practice, not just one isolated part of it. What's more each person creates their own level of fitness, so you can benefit from yoga whether you're seventeen or seventy, fit or unfit, used to exercise or totally inactive.

Those parts of the body which yoga strengthens dramatically are the back, stomach and lungs – simply because amongst the majority of us these are nearly always in pretty bad shape. If you decide to take up yoga for fitness and relaxation, you'll invariably find you can adapt a specific series of *asanas* or poses to suit your body's own needs, or alternatively you may decide to embark on a long and exploratory training which teaches you to practise the exercises as well as the philosophy of yoga more fully – including adopting a certain diet and lifestyle.

Whichever direction you decide to follow, yoga practice must be regular, at

Below left. The 'third eye' (2). Below. To refresh tired eyes (3).

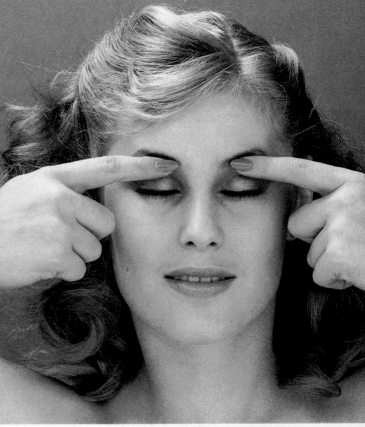

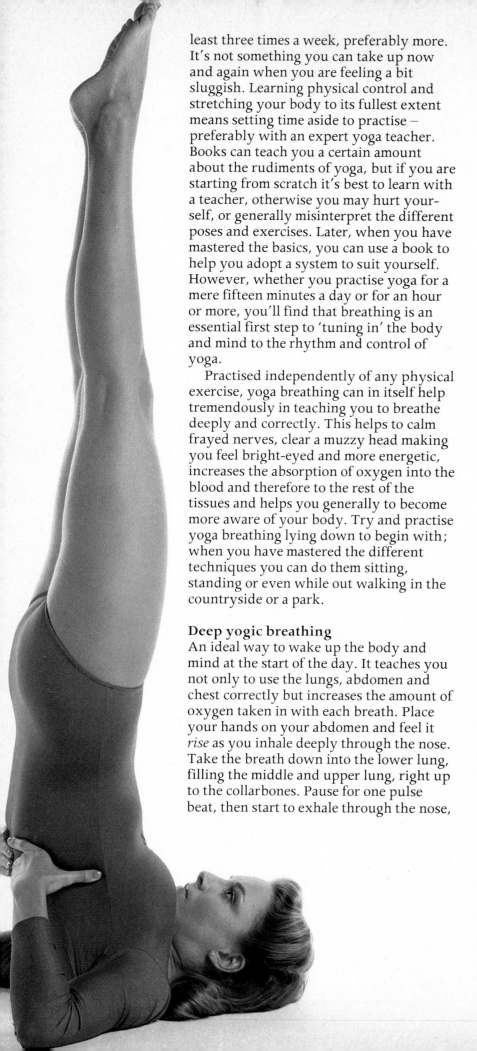

least three times a week, preferably more. It's not something you can take up now and again when you are feeling a bit sluggish. Learning physical control and stretching your body to its fullest extent means setting time aside to practise – preferably with an expert yoga teacher. Books can teach you a certain amount about the rudiments of yoga, but if you are starting from scratch it's best to learn with a teacher, otherwise you may hurt yourself, or generally misinterpret the different poses and exercises. Later, when you have mastered the basics, you can use a book to help you adopt a system to suit yourself. However, whether you practise yoga for a mere fifteen minutes a day or for an hour or more, you'll find that breathing is an essential first step to 'tuning in' the body and mind to the rhythm and control of yoga.

Practised independently of any physical exercise, yoga breathing can in itself help tremendously in teaching you to breathe deeply and correctly. This helps to calm frayed nerves, clear a muzzy head making you feel bright-eyed and more energetic, increases the absorption of oxygen into the blood and therefore to the rest of the tissues and helps you generally to become more aware of your body. Try and practise yoga breathing lying down to begin with; when you have mastered the different techniques you can do them sitting, standing or even while out walking in the countryside or a park.

Deep yogic breathing
An ideal way to wake up the body and mind at the start of the day. It teaches you not only to use the lungs, abdomen and chest correctly but increases the amount of oxygen taken in with each breath. Place your hands on your abdomen and feel it *rise* as you inhale deeply through the nose. Take the breath down into the lower lung, filling the middle and upper lung, right up to the collarbones. Pause for one pulse beat, then start to exhale through the nose,

emptying the lungs in the same slow smooth manner, pulling the abdomen well in towards the backbone as you breath out the last remnant of stale air. Most people feel so invigorated after they've practised their first few yogic breaths – both more alert, yet more relaxed – that they soon overcome any puny, shallow breathing habits. Finding you can increase your lung capacity is another delightful surprise which has invaluable health benefits. As you breathe in count silently up to two, hold the breath for a count of four, exhale for a count of eight. As your lungs get stronger you'll be able to build this up to counts of four, eight, sixteen, or even more – always remember to exhale for double the time you've held your breath. Don't do too many breaths when you first start, otherwise you might feel faint or dizzy from all that extra oxygen.

Tranquillizing breath or alternate nostril breathing
This should be done in the evening before bedtime, to help you relax and sleep well. Place the right thumb against the right nostril, closing it, then inhale through the left nostril for a count of eight, now hold the breathe for a count of eight, closing off the left nostril with your middle finger, then exhale through the right nostril for a count of eight. Inhale once more through the right nostril for a count of eight, hold for eight, exhale through the left nostril for eight; this completes one round. Try and keep the breathing rhythmic and continuous, repeating it for up to seven rounds. If you're tense, nervy, or headachy, this has an immediate calming effect.

MEDITATION the easy way to calmness and relaxation

If you are put off the idea of meditation by a vision of a lot of saffron-robed, shaven-headed devotees, endlessly chanting prayers in a cloud of incense, think again! You certainly don't have to join a religious sect, withdraw from the world or become a vegetarian in order to reap the benefits of simple meditation. What's more, as anyone who meditates regularly will tell you, not only does this type of 'switching off' do wonders for relaxing both mind and body, but by focusing the brain it increases mental alertness and concentration, and improves memory and overall energy. As a tool for fighting stress-related illnesses – migraine, asthma, insomnia, indigestion, high blood pressure – meditation can prove invaluable by exorcizing destructive nervous tension.

Simplicity and straightforwardness are the key to meditation, which makes it a technique that's instantly appealing and freely available to just about anyone. Most forms of meditation used in the West today are variations on basic Zen techniques, as practised over many centuries by Buddhist monks in China and Tibet. If you go to a school or a centre for meditation, you may be given a 'mantra' which is a short Sanskrit word or phrase chosen for it's deeply relaxing effect on both your conscious and subconscious levels of thought. However, in order to meditate successfully, you can just as easily devise your own 'key word' or rhyming phrase to help you get into a calm, reflective state of mind. Concentrating on a word or phrase is, after all, just a device to block out all other disturbing thoughts and problems which may come into your head, so just about anything will do such as 'romantic red roses', 'crisp crackly snow' or 'limpid languorous lagoon'. Have fun and make up your own mantra to suit yourself – but when you've found one, stick to it!

A yoga teacher might suggest using the word 'one' – similar to the mantra 'om' – simply counting from one to ten, or concentrating your attention on one specific object. Remember, however, hypnotic repetitiveness, not variety, is the object of your word-image, so don't get carried away with anything long-winded or fancy! When you first begin meditating, you will find that no matter how hard you concentrate on your word or mantra, your mind will start to stray to other things. Just nudge these 'intruders' gently out of your conscious mind and return your focus firmly to your key word. Eventually you will find that you can switch off and slip quite easily into a calm withdrawn state, pushing aside such worries as what to cook for supper or how much washing you've got to take down to the laundrette. Set aside the same ten to twenty minute period each day for meditation. First thing in the morning, lunchtime or early evening are ideal, but not just before bedtime, because meditating recharges your store of energy and will stop you sleeping.

MEDITATION TECHNIQUES

One
Make yourself comfortable, sitting on a chair or the floor, back upright. Ensure that each part of your body is relaxed. Close your eyes and become aware of your breathing. This should be deep to begin with, it will get shallower and softer as you become more relaxed. This is *not* a breathing exercise however. Don't follow any particular rhythm. As you exhale each time count silently or audibly the word 'one'. Savour the sound, image and feeling of the number, it's roundness and simplicity. Continue breathing, repeating this word over and over at your own pace until your meditation period is over.

One to ten
The same rules apply as above but instead of repeating the word 'one', build up the numbers from one to ten with each consecutive breath. Visualize the numbers each time you exhale by mentally 'planting' them in the centre of your tummy. Don't anticipate or rush the next number, just let one melt gently into two, two into three and so on each time you breathe out. Take as much time as you like to breathe, count and 'see' each number.

Pretty pictures
Place one small perfectly shaped object – a flower, a lit candle, a vase – in front of you at eye level. Concentrate on this while you breathe, stare at the object, giving it your 100 per cent undivided attention. Presently it will exert a pleasant hypnotic influence over you, losing its obvious everyday form, appearing surreal, shifting its image and outline. As they become more relaxed, some people see a glow and different colours surrounding the object, rather like a halo. Each time your mind begins to wander off onto other things, draw your concentration in closer to the object pinning it down until nothing else exists. An added benefit of this type of 'creative imagery' is that it often sharpens concentration and visual perception.

Whatever system of meditation you follow, proof of its success can only be experienced once you have finished meditating. Do you feel calm, rested, yet totally alert – all the advantages of a good night's sleep without any of the doziness? If so, your meditation is a success.

EXCERCISE—THE LONG AND THE SHORT OF IT

Exercise is possibly the most worthwhile long-term investment you can make in your health as well as your looks. Don't get carried away with the idea that exercise will make you slim if you're overweight – it won't. But it will strengthen, elongate, tone, and add contour to flabby, slack muscles and discourage you from putting on weight in the first place by helping your body burn up extra calories more efficiently. By increasing your intake of oxygen, speeding up the elimination of poisonous wastes and revving up the blood supply to every organ and tissue in the body, exercise will make your skin glow and look clearer and firm, help your eyes sparkle and improve the condition of nails and hair. Through regular exercise you will sleep better, enjoy greater physical and mental energy, and increase your reserves of stamina. Vigorous, regular exercise is the all-time enemy of stress (how can you worry about work when you're giving your all to complete the final mile through the park?). It releases pent-up muscular and nervous tension as well as helping the body flush away harmful stress chemicals which would otherwise be stored up in the body. Vital too in protecting you against more serious so-called 'ageing' diseases is the work-out given to heart, lungs and circulatory system (blood vessels and arteries) when you take exercise. Doctors now believe that small amounts of regular exercise can help reduce our risk of developing such common problems as heart diseases, hardening of the arteries, thrombosis and hypertension.

Yet if you aren't one of those lucky people who has been accustomed to doing sports or has taken an active interest in exercise all their lives, the idea of suddenly embarking on a keep-fit programme may seem unnecessarily daunting. Many people are put off the idea of exercise because they see it almost as a form of penance; gruelling physical labour which detracts from rather than adding to the enjoyment of life, yet exercise can and should be fun.

There is a type of exercise to suit every one of us depending on our personality, physical build, health and lifestyle. On the whole it's best to stick to an activity that you not only feel happy doing but manage reasonably well. Clearly, attempting to take up tennis in your mid-thirties or forties if you're unfit as well as a stranger to the tennis court is as unwise as it is unrealistic, since your chances of deriving either pleasure or fitness from it are few. Ideally any good all-round exercise should combine plenty of stretching movements to keep the muscles and limbs supple, all-out exertion to give the heart and lungs a full workout and raise the level of circulation, and rhythmical muscle contractions to strengthen all the main muscle groups. The types of exercise that incorporate all these are swimming, dancing – either jazz or ballet – general keep-fit exercises or gym practice. Jogging, running, skipping, dancing, fast cycling and swimming are the best forms of aerobic exercise – that's the sort that makes you puff and pant and break out in a sweat – while sports such as tennis and squash combine aerobics with specific muscle development. On the whole if you lead a stressful and rather competitive life it's best to steer clear of aggressive games like squash where the emphasis is on winning, as you could unconsciously add to your stress levels by trying to beat your opponent – or worse by losing the game! Dancing, cycling, running, fast walking, swimming and gym exercises are all good, non-competitive, all-round activities that allow you to set your own pace and therefore should suit just about everyone who basically wants to exercise in order to keep fit and trim rather than win or set new goals.

There's a different approach to fitness for different ages, and the way to go about your daily exercise depends on the state of your joints and muscles and how inactive or active you've been most of your life. Up to the age of twenty-five, provided you're healthy and fairly active (even walking a lot and climbing stairs instead of using the lift puts you in this category you'll be pleased to hear), you can take up any form of exercise, making sure however not to over-strain the body. Between the ages of twenty-five and thirty-four you may need to begin exercising in easy stages, especially if you're basically unfit, because the muscles and joints become less pliable

Regular exercise – a guarantee of long-term health and a beauty aid.

and start to stiffen up from the mid-twenties onward. After the age of thirty-five anybody who is unused to regular physical exercise should get their doctor's blessing before embarking on any vigorous exercise other than swimming or fast walking. But *whatever your age* remember that muscle strain and stiffness, sprains, torn ligaments – not to mention exhaustion – are all you can expect if you throw yourself into a new exercise programme in an effort to get fit overnight. Chances are

after the first flush of enthusiasm you'll give up the idea entirely. Whether you're used to sports and exercise or not, you should always treat your body with respect. Like anything else fitness needs careful cultivation and most athletes will tell you that you need to keep fit in order to jog – not the other way around.

Your body is not a piece of machinery that you can just switch on automatically to make it speed up and perform at your command. Don't forget that even the world's finest ballet dancers, gymnasts and sportswomen have to spend hours tuning up their bodies so that they will work at maximum efficiency with the minimum risk of physical damage. You must spend a few minutes warming up before you begin exercising; knee bends, waist stretches, arm swings, ankle rolls, running on the spot and lunges, are all essential for loosening up the main muscle groups. After exercising don't just come to a grinding halt and slump in a chair to relax. The body needs to be gently returned to its resting state to avoid shocking the muscles and the nervous system. It's like changing gears in a car, you don't go from fourth to neutral all in one go. Repeat the same sequence of warm-ups that you began with to wind down afterwards.

The time of day you choose to exercise is tremendously important both psychologically and physically. Virtuous as it may seem, it's no use trying to jog two miles around the park at six a.m. if you are fundamentally a 'night owl' who can't co-ordinate thought or action before ten a.m.! Taking exercise during the lunch hour if you have a busy working day makes sense especially if you're trying to avoid the temptation of overeating at lunchtime. Make sure you eat after, not before, exercising. Early evening is another excellent time to put aside for a physical workout as it should help you sleep soundly as well as encourage you to work off the tensions and frustrations of the day. It's a mistake to dismiss evening exercise because you think you're too tired. You may well become even more tired if you collapse at home in front of TV after a day's work, but thirty or forty-five minutes vigorous exercise will almost certainly wake you up and make you feel bright-eyed and alert. Exercise also stabilizes the emotions, especially negative harmful ones. Adrenalin and other stress hormones that accumulate as a result of stress syndromes are generally fully dispersed after a long run, swim, or an exercise class, and so you're less likely to be tempted into having a cigarette or a drink to calm you down and help you relax: exercise does this far more efficiently anyway. One word of warning however. No matter how strong or healthy you are stay tuned in to your own alarm system; if you develop any unusual feelings while you exercise such as nausea, headaches, dizziness, palpitations, chest pains, or cramp, stop immediately. Should these recur consult your doctor about the possible cause.

SPECIAL YEARS – THE TEENS

Every age you pass through brings with it it's own problems; shifts of emphasis in skincare, modifications to be made in make-up and specific figure problems caused by hormonal changes and a different lifestyle. Although the nature of the problems encountered between the ages of thirteen and twenty remain pretty consistent, the help available to counteract and cope with them is continually improving.

Someone who probably knows all there is to know about making the most of oneself at any age is Joan Price, beauty writer, lecturer, and founder of one of London's leading cosmetic advice centres. There's not a beauty problem in existence that Joan Price doesn't recognize – or know how to deal with.

The teens can be a time of confusion, and the most constructive thing any young girl can do to make the best of herself is to work out her potential. Does she have an easy, problem-free skin yet lank greasy hair, or figure problems and a tendency to spots with thick, shiny, manageable hair? Work out what your problems are and try to minimize them while making the most of your good points. We are rarely blessed with limitless patience in our teens and therefore often fail to give products or routines a chance to work. Skin improvements don't happen overnight, they do, however, materialize with proper washing and cleansing and the use of correct products to treat spots and open pores. You simply must stick to a good, simple skincare routine for at least three months before you can expect to see any improvement in your skin.

Teenage skin in the 1980s suffers from much the same turmoil and upheaval as it has in past decades. After all, the main cause of excessively greasy skin, spots, blackheads, as well as more severe acne, is the immense upswing in hormonal activity that begins in the early teens and often doesn't settle down into a definite pattern until the late teens or early twenties. During this period the sebaceous glands temporarily work overtime.

lumps and bumps that characterize more serious cystic acne you should certainly consult your doctor about the possibility of undergoing medical treatment to tackle the problem.

A florid complexion or one which flares up bright red when you enter a warm room can also cause agonies of embarassment when you are young and trying to appear cool and self-possessed. Those with fair, sensitive and dry skin usually suffer from this problem because the blood vessels and capillaries are closer to the surface of the skin. One solution is to wear a light colourless foundation and blend in a very small amount of pale, putty beige cover cream (the sort normally used to cover blemishes and under eye circles) to 'cool' the offending areas. Avoid green powders and creams though, they generally look obvious and don't hide your flushes nearly so well.

In the teens your make-up kit should be kept small and simple; especially if you are lucky enough to have good natural colouring. You may need a lightly-tinted moisturizer to even out skin colour or cover up the occasional blemish, and for special evenings out you might want to use a light camouflage cream to minimize dark shadows under the eyes; sometimes more a problem of heredity than late nights! Freckles look pretty and give a fresh, outdoor appearance, but if you hate them use a golden-tinted moisturizer or gel to 'blend' them together. Tinted lip gloss is ideal for adding a slight sheen and a hint of colour to the lips instead of over-emphasizing the mouth with lipstick. For parties you can softly accentuate the eyes with a neutral sludgy eye shadow – plum, beige, grey and brown are best – and add a trace of mascara to make the lashes look thicker, darker and longer. But remember, a young face looks its most appealing when the overall effect is fresh and translucent, each feature perfectly balanced, never obviously made-up.

Although teenage skincare consists very largely of scrupulous cleansing, washing and surface peeling to control oiliness and prevent pore problems, there are times – for instance during very cold windy weather or if your school or home is over centrally-heated – when the surface of the skin may feel slightly taut, and prone to flaking and chapping. That's when a simple lightweight cold cream or an oil-free moisturizing lotion can help by putting a fine layer between the dry air and your skin.

In order to prevent the open pores becoming blocked with dead skin, try using a mildly abrasive facial washing pad or a soft brush to skim off all surface debris. Ordinary spots can usually be kept under control by using one of the excellent medicated, sulphur- or camphor-based treatments available, especially formulated for problem skins, but it's a mistake to start taking strong medicines for surface pustular acne. Most beauty salons and trained therapists can treat these spots and pimples very effectively with surface peeling and deep cleansing, and also by suggesting the right sorts of healing and drying lotions to use at home. Try to use a soap, cleanser and healing cream from the same range, as they are all designed to work together. If you do suffer from the very enlarged, red, sometimes painful

GRACEFUL MIDDLE YEARS

Use a lightweight foundation and colourless translucent powder to even out skin colour.

The term 'middle-aged' sounds strangely out of date nowadays, when styles in hair, clothes and make-up have reached the ultimate in easy-to-wear casual smartness that looks as good on someone of twenty as on someone of forty-five. Have you noticed also how so many women manage to look prettier, more confident and relaxed – more youthful even – than they did in their teens and twenties? Perhaps this is simply because self-assurance and knowing what suits you is something that can only develop over years of experiment to discover how to make the most of your colouring, skin type, figure and features. This of course doesn't mean wearing the same eyeshadow, blusher and lipstick at forty as you did at twenty-two. In fact nothing is more ageing than wearing the same make-up as you did then or five years ago. Not only will those same colours and textures probably not suit you any longer – they'll also be out of fashion and look desperately dated!

Although the latest outrageous make-up gimmicks are not for you if you're much over thirty or thirty-five, do keep an eye open for the newest colours and formulas which can enhance – not swamp – your own features. Nothing can beat well applied make-up to help you look your best as you get older. No matter how flawless or attractive a woman's face, good make-up can only make her look more attractive, radiant and probably younger.

As you get older skin tone often gets sallower, greyer, more uneven and marred by patches of darker pigmentation, broken red veins and weathering. This is where a lightweight fluid, tinted foundation works wonders in evening out and brightening skin colour without giving a flat, matt, powdery effect. Choose a tint that's as similar as possible to your own skin tone and which blends in quickly to give a semi-opaque coverage : just enough to hide tiny flaws and blemishes and impart a healthy radiance to the skin. This doesn't mean lashing out on an expensive product. You can get very reasonably priced make-up these days that offers a wide range of shades and textures. Powder should always be colourless and translucent to avoid caking, settling into facial lines and creases, and altering your foundation tone.

For enlarging and defining the eyes, concentrate on the natural colour pigments such as grey, brown, taupe, beige, sage; tones that you'll find naturally in human skin under different lights. Bright, colourful eyeliners and shadows should be kept for parties and evening wear, when strong artificial lights drain the face of gentler colours. Upbeat purples, mauves, blues, greens and brick-browns tend to look hard and draw attention to lines and crêpeyness around the eyes. Frosted powders also act as a rather cruel spotlight, focusing on wrinkles and slack skin, so it's best to stick to matt blushers, eye shadows and highlighters after a certain age. Powder generally in all its different forms is easier to apply and gives a smoother, more long-

lasting finish to make-up than the messier cream rouges and liquid eyeshadows, 'polishes' and highlighters that often give an uneven 'blobby' effect.

If you like to outline your eyes along the rim of the lashes you'll avoid any hard-edge definition by using a very soft, waxy kohl crayon or eye pencil that glides on in soft focus without pulling at the delicate skin around the eyes. Crayon gives a softly blurred line as opposed to liquid or cake liner which can look unduly severe. Very

bright lipsticks can make even a young face look pinched, hard and garish – but on a more mature face or lips that are lined they look positively grotesque. Outline the mouth with a neutral toned crayon – beige, dark brown, earthy red – then choose a sheer and creamy, slightly frosted tawny, beige pink, coral or peachy lipstick. Avoid so-called 'hot' pinks, 'dead' purply-browns and reds, pillarbox scarlet or blue-reds, which dry and stain the lips, add ten years to virtually any face and drain it of colour.

Softer, natural tones are best for shading and shaping. Harsh colours will emphasize wrinkles and make the face seem pinched.

SKINCARE

The biggest bonus of getting older is that the skin often settles into a calm trouble-free period after the ups and downs of the teens and twenties. Acne, blackheads, excessive oiliness, pimples have generally run their course by the time you reach your early thirties. As you learn the method of skincare that is best suited to you, you're less likely to flounder around and will be more 'in charge' of the regular attention required by your skin type. Even though skin gets drier as the years go by, the basic rules of deep cleansing, toning, moisturizing and nourishing still apply, although you may decide to change the type of products you use. Again, as with make-up, it's a mistake to think that spending more money on exotic or overpriced creams and lotions will prevent your skin from showing natural signs of age, because they won't – whatever the advertisments say!

Spending money at a beauty salon to have facials is only worthwhile if just for a change you want someone else to do for your skin what you should be doing for it yourself. However, if you lead a very active and busy life without much time to spend on home routines, a monthly facial will certainly help your skin to look fresher and better groomed – but probably no younger! This is because beauty therapists do use some extremely effective appliances to help them steam, deep cleanse, refine, brighten and soften the skin. For instance, a mild galvanic current (cathiordermie) helps creams and lotions penetrate the epidermis more effectively while rotating face brushes stimulate the circulation, and also encourage products to be absorbed by the skin.

As you get older you're bound to notice that certain areas of your face and body seem to age faster and in a different way to others – no matter how well you look after them. Being clued up and prepared for these gradual changes can help you cope with them more effectively and even slow down the rate at which they occur.

Upper lip
Tiny vertical creases that form along the upper lip sometimes creating a blurred or jagged lipline usually start to form sometime in the forties. These are often caused by puckering up the mouth or by smoking. Make sure you apply protective moisturizer at all times, and blend your foundation well into the lipline and powder before outlining the mouth.

Eyes
The fine skin around the eyes can begin to show crow's feet, 'laughter lines', bags, dark circles and crêpeyness as early as the mid- or late twenties. Avoid too much sunbathing and always protect the skin with a good sunscreen and use a lightweight eye cream at night and plenty of moisturizer under your make-up. Have your eyesight checked regularly to avoid screwing up the eyes and try to wear good sunglasses in bright, glaring light and sunny weather. Minimize dark lines and circles with a trace of buff coloured concealer stick on top of your foundation, and make sure you get enough sleep so you don't cultivate shadows in the first place. Puffiness and 'bags' under the eyes can be caused by fluid retention – especially while you sleep – so use compresses soaked in ice-cold witch hazel, eyebright herbal tea, or an eye tonic to decongest the area and remember not to use too much eye cream at night as this can also puff up the skin.

Neck
The skin on the throat, neck and chest is often a prime giveaway of age becoming rough, discoloured and marked with horizontal 'necklace' lines usually through poor posture, wearing rough polo-necked sweaters, too much sunbathing and lack of proper moisturizing. Avoid this by carrying through *all* your usual facial treatments onto the neck area, particularly your moisturizer and night cream which should be extended right down to the collar-bones to prevent crêpeyness and lines from developing. A good clay-based mask used once or twice a month tightens and brightens the skin, counteracting dingy or yellow skin tones and refining the pores. From the age of thirty onwards a rich body cream or baby lotion smoothed in after bathing will help to keep the skin soft and supple.

Hands
The paper fine skin on the backs of the hands is particularly prone to dehydration and pigment problems from the mid- to late forties onwards. Keep the skin well cossetted by using hand cream every time you put your hands into water and by wearing an effective sunscreen when you go out into the sun. 'Liver spots', those dark mottled patches that appear after

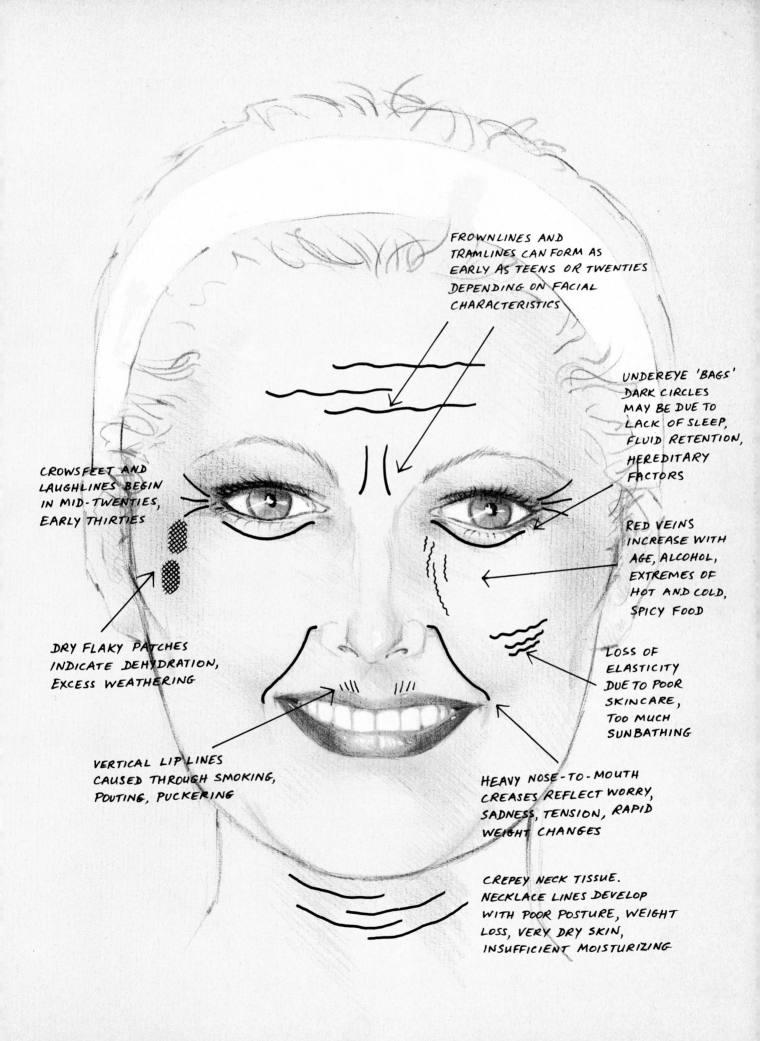

FROWNLINES AND
TRAMLINES CAN FORM AS
EARLY AS TEENS OR TWENTIES
DEPENDING ON FACIAL
CHARACTERISTICS

UNDEREYE 'BAGS'
DARK CIRCLES
MAY BE DUE TO
LACK OF SLEEP,
FLUID RETENTION,
HEREDITARY
FACTORS

CROWSFEET AND
LAUGHLINES BEGIN
IN MID-TWENTIES,
EARLY THIRTIES

RED VEINS
INCREASE WITH
AGE, ALCOHOL,
EXTREMES OF
HOT AND COLD,
SPICY FOOD

DRY FLAKY PATCHES
INDICATE DEHYDRATION,
EXCESS WEATHERING

LOSS OF
ELASTICITY
DUE TO POOR
SKINCARE,
TOO MUCH
SUNBATHING

VERTICAL LIP LINES
CAUSED THROUGH SMOKING,
POUTING, PUCKERING

HEAVY NOSE-TO-MOUTH
CREASES REFLECT WORRY,
SADNESS, TENSION, RAPID
WEIGHT CHANGES

CREPEY NECK TISSUE.
NECKLACE LINES DEVELOP
WITH POOR POSTURE, WEIGHT
LOSS, VERY DRY SKIN,
INSUFFICIENT MOISTURIZING

about the age of fifty, are something of a mystery to dermatologists and unfortunately once they develop there's little you can do to shift them. A good bleaching cream may help to fade them slightly and a strong sunblock will prevent the sun from making them worse.

Stretch marks
One of the possible results of pregnancy (especially if you gain a lot of extra weight), is the appearance of fine white or silvery lines caused by overstretching and rupturing of the skin's surface. These can appear on the tummy, hips, thighs and breasts and cannot be removed once they've formed – so take care generally not to go through extreme yo-yo weight changes. Regular massage with a good body cream or oil helps keep the skin supple and conditioned during pregnancy.

Wrinkles and lines
A famous American beautician once said that a face without lines is like a book without words – and it's easy enough to appreciate her point, since few of us over the age of twenty-five would like a blank, vacuous, mask-like face, no matter how pretty it was. As we pass out of our teens, all of us inevitably develop a few lines and facial marks that distinguish individual character and personality. These are, after all, a natural and unavoidable side effect of the way we move and use our faces to talk, smile, eat, laugh and think; expression lines which start to etch themselves onto the face from the twenties on, and gradually become deeper and more pronounced over the years. The lines and wrinkles that you *should* try to prevent forming prematurely are those that result from skin damage. Too much sunbathing, very dry atmospheres, cold icy winds, smoking, drinking a lot of alcohol and crash dieting can all too easily lead to dehydrated, papery skin, the formation of deep wrinkles and creases on the cheeks, and a loss of elasticity and firm facial contours. Caused by an excessive reduction in the skin's moisture level and the destruction of its collagen and elastic fibres, there is nothing you can do to remove these signs of age once they've appeared. They can, however, be minimized by using a rich daytime moisturizer under your make-up and massaging a deep-acting treatment cream into the face and neck at night. There are also some very effective so-called 'shock treatments' and 'cures' on the market,

creams and serums designed to be used over a two-or three-week period to soften and smooth very dry skin and plump out lines. Deep moisturizing masks which can be applied all over the eye area also help to condition the skin, while, for the odd special occasion you can apply a temporary 'anti-wrinkle' gel or cream which subtly smoothes out wrinkles and tightens loose contours by covering the skin with a fine translucent film. It is very difficult to firm up the chin and cheek area and the skin around the mouth once the muscles have become slack and the skin has lost its resilience. Using a small electronic facial massage unit can help to tone lazy muscles and tighten the area – but only if you do this promptly and regularly. Exercising generally – particularly keep fit, gym and dance classes – helps to keep facial contours firm and supple while increasing the supply of blood to the skin, giving the skin a healthier, less lined appearance.

Figure problems
Our general metabolism – the rate at which we burn up the food we eat – starts to slow down significantly from the age of thirty-five onwards, although to what degree depends on how far we allow our lifestyles to become less active and more sedentary. It's around this age that you should avoid gaining extra weight as it becomes increasingly difficult to shed the surplus pounds you acquire in later years. Areas that are notoriously liable to 'fill out' are the waist, tummy, hips, thighs and buttocks, since women carry an extra layer of fatty tissue on these parts of the body. Try and trim your eating habits to suit your energy demands and remember that eating more food without compensating by taking extra physical activity to burn it up will most certainly mean that you put on pounds and inches where you don't want them. Resist the urge to indulge in snacks between meals and buns, chocolates, biscuits, sweets, ice cream, sweet drinks and alcohol. Adopt a regular exercise programme that you enjoy to help firm the muscles, banish flab and burn up calories. Specific problems such as a slack or drooping bustline, spare waist 'tyre' or wads of fat on thighs and hips can be improved by doing gym exercises that strengthen and whittle down those areas, going to a health club that offers 'spot reduction' treatments usually in the form of intensive massage, or attending keep-fit classes which have a general effect.

After the early or mid-thirties, lines and wrinkles tend to develop as a natural and largely unavoidable result of facial movements and loss of skin moisture. These can be minimized by using good moisturizers, treatment creams and conditioning masks.

INDEX